D1613202

WICKED VICTORIANS

WICKED
VICTORIANS

An anthology of
clandestine literature
of the nineteenth century
compiled and edited by
Gordon Grimley

THE ODYSSEY PRESS
LONDON

Published by The Odyssey Press,
2, Bramber Road, West Kensington, London W.14.
A division of Penthouse International

printed by
Willmer Brothers Limited, Birkenhead
and bound by
C. Tinling & Co. Ltd.,
Liverpool, London, Prescot

SBN 850 95120 8

CONTENTS

Introduction

Anthologies are normally intended to encapsulate man's finest literary endeavours. This one is a small monument to his perversities, yet it is also a key to an age.

Just as one could look at England today from entirely different viewpoints, so in the year 1862 two men looked at England through different windows. 'We may not be more moral, more imaginative, nor better educated than our ancestors', said the catalogue of London's International Exhibition, 'but we have more steam, gas, railways and power-looms, while there are more of us and we have more to spend'. In less naive prose, Henry Mayhew prefaced the fourth volume of his *London Labour and the London Poor* with the words: 'I enter upon this part of my subject with a deep sense of the misery, the vice, the ignorance and the want that encompasses us on every side. . . .'

The unknown catalogue scribe had conjured up a miniature manifesto of middle and upper class thought. In that same year Henry Mayhew, one of history's great reporters, went beyond the screen of this self-appraisal to show how tens of thousands of Victorians lived in unthinkably hideous conditions, dragging out their sad existences from birth to death. 'My poor people', wrote Queen Victoria herself, of the dwellers in the Black Country. One can scarcely conjecture what she might have thought had the foetid slum-warrens within a carriage-trot from Buckingham Palace been opened up to her.

The underside of a nation so divisive in its wealth, resources and classes was one of widespread drunkeness, cheap popular literature, theft, and prostitution. 'In 1857, according to the best authorities', wrote Mayhew, 'there were 8,600 prostitutes known to the police, but this is far from being even an approximate return of the loose women in the metropolis. It scarcely does more than record the circulating harlotry of the Haymarket and Regent Street' ... We have before stated the assumed number of prostitutes in London to be about 80,000 and, large as this total may appear, it is not improbable that it is below the reality rather than above it'.

There was yet a bridge between Mayhew's realities and the hedged dwellings of upper suburbia. It was formed by the most concentrated efflorescence of pornographic literature in our history which, in the forms of books, pamphlets and magazines, attracted not only those whose wallets were full, but their servants also: 'There are book-hawkers', said Mayhew in his same fourth volume, 'who go about the country, having first filled their wallets from the filthy cellars of Holywell street, sowing the seeds of immorality; servants in country houses will pay, without hesitation, large prices for such improper books'.

Improper was a mild term for any Victorian to have used of such literature—even Mayhew, the sort of man who could have switched in time from one century to the next with scarcely a blink.

We are, then, here in a context of a form of society which has been too glibly labelled 'repressive' by superficial observers. The long-held picture of conditions of apparent sexual restraint begins to fade when we view the Victorian pyramid from the bottom. 'Woman in the abstract', said R. J. Cruikshank in *Charles Dickens and Early Victorian England* (1949) 'was as radiant as an angel, as dainty as a fairy—she was a picture on the wall, a statue in a temple, a being whose physical processes were an inscrutable mystery'. This of course was the Victorian moral establishment's melange of social propaganda and hypocrisy disguised as belief, for while the social suppression at certain levels of normal and instinctual activities was certainly a factor that prodded the emergence of a Porno-Atlantis, it was not the prime cathartic. The ratio of erotic and pornographic literature to repressive states of society, is not a constant; it provides

8

no scale whereby we can measure this sector of man's requirements and activities. In America today, where the commercial exploitation of sex takes every form—from phallic 'novelties' to soi-disant underground journals mainly of erotic-scatological content; from endless 'nudie movies' to cheap paperbacks—still there is a considerable public for erotic and pornographic literature. Ironically, it includes numerous reprints of Victorian pornography.

For a great part of the population of Victorian England, morality was scarcely skin-deep. Of the twelve-acre, gaslit pleasure gardens at Cremorne—in what is now the Chelsea-Fulham area—the surgeon William Acton wrote in his *Prostitution* (1857): 'On and around that platform waltzed, strolled and fed some thousand souls—perhaps seven hundred of them men of the upper and middle classes, the remainder prostitutes more or less *prononcées* ... they seemed to touch and go, like ants in a hurry of business'. *The Lancet* said in 1857 that one house in every sixty was a brothel. In his 'Apology for our Title' in the first issue of the pornographic monthly magazine *The Pearl* (July 1879 to December 1880), the Editor wrote that one of the names suggested for it was *The Cremorne*. It was after all a name that at no long stretch could be construed as a phallic pun. 'Every hundred steps one jostles twenty harlots', wrote the moderate, sensible Taine of the metropolis in his *Notes on England* (1872).

The brief carriage trot from the royal palace to London's reeking slums, to the bawdy houses and the tens of thousand of 'gay' girls (the euphemism, then, for prostitutes), aptly symbolized the almost mythical distance that separated the prim, delicate girl of outward imagery from the undernourished girl slaves of the capital's manufactories on whom leisured men like Walter preyed.

Walter, the otherwise anonymous author of *My Secret Life*—the most sexually detailed of all autobiographies—stands with his contemporary, Henry Spencer Ashbee, as the dominating symbolic figures of the vast sub-world of Victorian sexuality. Walter's philosophy was simple, but extensive: 'You can talk any woman randy', he confidently tells us in his 4,200 page life story, as if in self-abnegating explanation of his complete sexual possession of scores of hundreds of girls and women. For Walter the concept of hearth, home and radiant woman-angel could be expressed in four letters.

The bibliographer, folklorist and essayist, Gershon Legman has proposed in his learned and fascinating work *The Horn Book* (1964) the theory that Walter and Ashbee were one and the same. His evidence is at once skilful and flimsy, befitting a good barrister defending a weak case. Ashbee was the author-compiler of the three volume bibliography of erotica and pornography which he caused to be privately printed in three extensive volumes. The greater part of his work—still the cornerstone of studies in this area —is extant in *Forbidden Books of the Victorians* (Odyssey Press, London, ed. Peter Fryer, 1970).

The most elementary considerations of the lives of these two strange men deny G. Legman's ingenious thesis. What Ashbee dreamed, Walter performed, and what Walter performed Henry Spencer Ashbee—business man, traveller, dedicated book collector and author of several books and many articles—would scarce have had time to commence. Their styles of writing were utterly divergent. To read Ashbee's footnotes to his bibliography (often occupying more of the page than the text) or his *Travels in Tunisia*, is to apprehend the unbridgeable chasm that lay between their characters and activities. Moreover, no bookman's recorded life— and Walter described his own from childhood to late middle-age— could have avoided allusive, subtle references to the then extensive literature of the very subject that Walter was eternally practising in his endless pick-ups, copulations and group orgies. A mental picture of Ashbee, incredibly energetic as he was, endlessly haunting likely streets, seducing, procuring and accosting women in age groups from fifteen to forty-five years of age and hurtling home to Bedford Square to studiously record and meticulously describe *An Essay on Women* is as acceptable as the thought of a cold bath in the rain.

The lives and pursuits of Ashbee and Walter conjoin to indicate that in a considerable part of Victorian society, no vast gulf obtained between the idea and the reality. For every heroine of Victorian pornography there was a living, breathing counterpart in Walter's told experiences:

'Look in the glass' I said pointing to the cheval mirror. 'You can see yourself there'—'Lor!' she said, 'to think there's houses with all this. Are there many such? Oh what a scream for us to be look-ing at ourselves like this!' 'Don't you like looking?' 'Yes, but it makes me too quick. We look very beautiful though, don't we?'

'Oh what a scream', indeed—for it was precisely this lusty, gusty,

'now-girls' approach to sex that was exemplified in much Victorian
writing of the genre. Books such as *Venus in India*—the best English
novel of its kind after *Fanny Hill*—represented what might be
termed 'healthy pornography', with never a nasty moment. The girls
in such novels come to sex with the bubbling eagerness of a child
approaching the sound of the sea: a metaphor which, if apparently fey,
was intended by the scribes of the time. These 'Queens of Pornotopia' enjoy their endless copulations with the frank, conscienceless
air of a thirsty man swilling good beer. Admirably—for the apparently dreaming reader—they combine born feminine appeal with a
sort of jolly lust, and their approach to the male organ is as of a girl
finding a long-desired new dress. At this level of creation they
descend only to minor perversions, rarely committing incest (the
ne plus ultra of many such books); if they do, it is with the same
carefree air of spooning yet another ice cream.

Such literature did not merely oppose the moral establishment,
nor offer up a sexual boo; it reversed the order of things, as a
woman might change a room around without adding or subtracting
a single article of furniture; it was—it might be thought—a form
of protest literature (whether conscious or not), *not* against the
known and all-too-visible realities, but against the public face of life,
against the images of 'improving literature', against the melting
Technicolor of the home novels, all of which denied the reality.
As *Private Eye* is to the *Daily Mail*, so it can be arguably extended
was *The Pearl* to *The Family Friend*. As the cheap, popular literature of the time had its 'sweet, golden-haired child', so *The Romance
of Lust* had its incredible orgies of incest. Both worlds lived, in
Steven Marcus's apt term, 'on the brink of the meaningless', each
with opposite intent, and each clutching a commercial bonus. The
poor bought the cheap, popular literature; the well-fed collected the
bound volumes of erotica and pornography.

Not only did this outpouring of literature represent a seemingly
planned outrage upon the moral establishment, but it created a new
genre of erotic literature and an 'improved' erotic vocabulary which
produced, *inter alia*, more synonyms for the male and female sex
organs than for any other objects in our language, whether common
or cant. The penis became a 'steed', a 'charger', a 'stallion', a
'piercer', a 'life-giving tube', and so endlessly on, and while this
veiling, this desperate searching for yet another way of express-
ing the obvious obtained a long and earlier tradition, it was the

Victorians who made of it an almost fine art. Even the French paid them the compliment in this area of translating some of their pornographia. Thus *My Grandmother's Tale; or May's Account of her Introduction to the Art of Love*, which appeared both as a separate novel and as a serial in *The Pearl*, took on a third life span in French in 1911 as *Mary, Kate et Suzey*. Books such as the four-volume *Romance of Lust* were not left untranslated for long, and there are times when the bibliographic trail becomes so long and tortuous that it is extremely difficult to decide whether, for instance, *My Married Life*—the most crapulous, illiterate and ill-written book I have ever read—is a translation from *Autour du Mariage de Paulette*, or vice versa. Since it is unthinkable that anyone capable of penning the sequence of public-toilet-wall scribblings that comprise the 'English' version could have had the intelligence to master a translator's knowledge of French, one is forced to conclude that a French printer/publisher made at least a slight improvement to it.

I have said that only the well-fed could afford these books, though among the lower classes, the cheap 'part' publications of some pornographic novels found added circulation. We are fortunate that Ashbee did not omit to mention prices wherever possible. Thus Edward Sellon's anonymous erotic autobiography appeared from the notorious pornographic publisher, William Dugdale, in 1867 for two guineas, as did *The New Ladies' Tickler* (1866), for both of which Sellon designed coloured lithographs, though according to Ashbee they were not very good ones. *Lady Bumtickler's Revels*, of the same period, was to be had for 'one guinea plain, or a guinea and a half in colours', while *The Power of Mesmerism* (?1880) carried a price of '3½ guineas' on its wrapper. This last title is one of those which pop up in several languages, there having been several French editions (*Le Magnisateur Libertin*) and at least one German edition (*Der Hypnotiseur*), which is evidently a rewritten version since its contents do not accord with Ashbee's description of the English edition. Since no copyright can obtain in pornography, it is the fate of the more ingenious stories to be thus used and re-used, translated and re-translated (often from a different language to the original), so that not only do names and venues change, but the plots also. Such books undergo a series of reincarnations which ensure the original story-line for a far longer and, indeed, more international life that that of many legitimate novels in the public domain. Such a book also is *Eveline*, of which the most cursory research reveals half a dozen editions, the longest and most detailed being *A Modern Eveline* of which the British Museum possesses the beautifully-bound three-volume edition in full crushed blue morocco, from the Dawes bequest. Curiously this version has reverted to the short-title *Eveline* in the two-volume Brandon House paperback edition (U.S.A.).

It should be remarked that, as with *A Modern Eveline,* the production standard of some late Victorian pornographic novels was remarkably high. *The New Ladies' Tickler* shows every sign of careful composition and imposition, as does *Leaves from An Old Escritoire* (c. 1885 to c. 1890), a very pretty piece of typography surpassed only by *Rosa Rogers* (c. 1898), possibly an American production. With books such as these last two, one is tempted to believe from the naive and ill-written nature of the contents, that the proud author paid for the production. In this entire genre of sub-literature, moreover, one author often paid the other the compliment of a 'mention'. Thus in a serialized novel *Sub-Umbra, or Sport Among the She-Noodles* which ran in several issues of *The Pearl,* there is a scene in which the sexually ebullient young Frank and his friend take home two sisters they have just seduced. Papa, Mama and the servants being asleep, the quartet join Frank's sister, Annie, and her friend, Rosa:

> 'All right', exclaimed Annie, 'my dears, everything is free between us and the boys, but we mean to punish you for allowing the impudent fellows to presume upon such liberties with you in the cave. Your bottoms shall smart, young ladies, I can assure you', as (sic) she produced a couple of light birch rods from a drawer; in fact, I had provided them for her, the idea having been suggested to me by reading a book called *The Romance of Lust*'.

This extract appeared in January 1880, while *The Romance of Lust* had appeared in four volumes between 1873 and 1876.

A very curious cross-reference in *Randiana* (c. 1884) leads into a deeper maze. In Chapter 19 (*Concerning Sixty-Nine; Or, The Magic Influence of the Tongue*) there is a reference to: 'Jack Wilton, the greatest essayist on cunt in an analytical form, who ever lived', and an immediate quotation from *The Horn Book: the Girl's Guide to the Knowledge of Good and Evil*, which was supposedly not, however, printed until fifteen years later! Moreover, when the extraordinary autobiographical novel, *Suburban Souls* appeared in 1901, the author who refers to himself only as 'Jackie S...' avers that he has been correcting the proofs of *The Horn Book** in the year of its publication. Such, then, is the bibliographical web of what to the layman often appears to be the simple, throwaway world of 'dirty books'.

The worlds of the Victorians were as manifold as our own. For decades their social approaches were scorned, their aesthetics were derided. We have learned to give the former a more comprehending study; we have revived—at least in the areas of typography and decoration—some of their richly-styled designs. In *Wicked Victorians* we open pages of greater strangeness, reflecting fantasies of quite another tinge from the defensively 'X'-blazoned manifestations of today; fantasies that (as we have learned from Mayhew, Walter and Ashbee—though primarily in the bibliophile's footnotes), had yet passed through the school of reality.

All of the material in this anthology preserves the punctuation and style of the originals.

G.G.

---

* This point is examined further in *Suburban Souls* (Odyssey Press, London, 1971).

The Pearl

Journal of Facetiae and Voluptuous Reading proclaimed the sub-title to this extraordinary magazine which appeared monthly between July 1879 and December 1886, proclaiming its imprint, in typically impudent style, as *Oxford: Printed at the University Press*. The entire run, in three volumes, contained 36 obscene coloured lithographs—of 'vile execution', says Ashbee. One detects perhaps a note of annoyance rather than of pure description in that phrase, and doubtless the Editor could afford no better.

The contents of *The Pearl* comprised six serialized novels, a number of short stories, and numerous ballads, poems, 'gossip' notes and anecdotes, amassing a total of over five hundred pages. Some items were simply cribbed, as for instance a translated extract from the early nineteenth century novel *Julie, ou j'ai sauvé ma rose**, by the Comtesse Felicité de Choiseul-Meuse which appeared under the title, *An Adventure with a Tribade; Related in a Letter from a Young Lady to Her Sister*. Some minor talents were occasionally displayed, as in a few parodies of Burns' *Merry Muses,* and some of the novels appeared separately in later years. Thus, *My grandmother's*

---

* *Julie,* trans. Dorothy Albertyn (Odyssey Press, London, 1970)

Tale; or May's Account of Her Introduction to the Art of Love is traceable many years later in a French edition, *Mary, Kate et Suzey*, listed by Perceau in his *Bibliographie du Roman Erotique au dix-neuvième siècle*.

The Pearl was neither the first nor the last of its kind. Its principal predecessors were *The Rambler* (1824–5) and *The Exquisite* (1842–4). In the previous century there had appeared the relatively long-lived journal *The Bon Ton Magazine* which endured for five volumes between March 1791 and March 1796.

Ashbee noted four volumes which were serial in every respect with *The Pearl*: *Swivia; or the Briefless Barrister*, issued in 1879 as an 'Extra Special Number'; *The Haunted House* (1880), with more 'vile lithographs'; *The Pearl Christmas Annual* (1881) and *The Erotic Casket Gift Book for 1882*. Although this completed the magazine's run, the Editor went on to produce *The Cremorne*—a title that he had earlier considered and rejected for *The Pearl*—and *The Boudoir* (1883), which again did not survive beyond the first issue.

This form of publishing does not appear to have survived the late Victorian period though a tenuous sociological comparison might be drawn between *The Pearl* and a few of the soi-disant 'underground' journals which in recent years have appeared with mainly crapulous and unquotable titles in the U.S.A. These however tend to be 'news sheets' imitative of the journalistic and typographical manner of the tabloid Press; there is no sense of continuity between issues and they are utterly lacking in that 'literary' touch which *The Pearl*, despite the obscenity of the greater part of its contents, somehow retained.

Here are reproduced extracts from two serials together with a number of verses. The first extract illustrates the widespread addiction to flagellation fantasies which occurs throughout Victorian literature of this kind.

MISS COOTE'S CONFESSION

Or the Voluptuous Experiences of an Old Maid;
In a series of Letters to a Lady Friend.

LETTER I

My Dear Girl,

I know I have long promised you an account of the reason of my penchant for the rod, which, in my estimation, is one of the most voluptuous and delicious institutions of private life, especially to a supposed highly respectable old maid like your esteemed friend. Treaties must be carried out, and promises kept, or how can I ever hope for the pleasure of making you taste my little green tickler again? Writing, and especially a sort of confession of my voluptuous weakness, is a most unpleasant task, as I feel as shamefaced in putting these things on paper as when my grandfather's housekeeper first bared my poor blushing little bottom to his ruthless attack. My only consolation at commencing is the hope that I shall warm to the subject as it progresses, in my endeavour to depict, for your gratification, some of the luscious episodes of my early days.

My grandfather, as you well know, was the celebrated Indian General, Sir Eyre Coote, almost as well known for his eight-penny fiasco with the Bluecoat boys as for his services to the Hon. E. I. Company. He was a confirmed martinet, and nothing delighted him so much as a good opportunity for the use of the cat, but I cannot tell you anything about that, as that was before my time. My first recollection of him is after the aforesaid City scandal, when he had to retire from public life in comparative disgrace. My parents both died when I was just upon twelve years of age, and the old General, who had no other relatives to care for, took entire charge of me, and, at his death, I was left his sole heiress, and mistress of nearly £3,000 per annum.

He resided in a quiet country house some twenty miles from London, where I spent the first few months of my orphaned life, with only his housekeeper, Mrs. Mansell, and the two servants, Jane and Jemima. The old General being away in Holland searching, so I afterwards heard, for original editions respecting the practices of Cornelius Hadrien, a curious work on the flagellation of religious penitents by a father confessor.

It was the middle of summer when he returned, and I soon found the liberty I had been enjoying considerably restricted. Orders not to pluck the flowers, or the fruit in the garden; and a regular lesson set me every day by the old autocrat himself. At first they were tolerably simple, but gradually increased in difficulty, and now, in after years, I can plainly understand his wolf and lamb tactics, by which I must eventually fall under his assumed just displeasure.

What gave me considerable pleasure at this time was his decided objection to mourning, or anything at all sombre in my dress. He said my parents had been shown every possible respect by wearing black for months, and I must now be dressed as became a young lady of my good expectations.

Although we scarcely ever received company, and then only some old fogy of his military acquaintance, I was provided with a profusion of new and elegant dresses, as well as beautiful shoes, slippers, drawers, and underlinen, all trimmed with finest lace &c., not even forgetting some very beautiful garters, a pair of which with gold buckles, he would insist upon putting on for me, taking no notice of my blushing confusion, as he pretended to arrange my drawers and skirts afterwards, but merely to remark: What a fine figure I should make, if they ever had to strip me for punishment.

Soon my lessons began to be harder than I could fairly manage. One day he expostulated, 'Oh! Rosa; Rosa!! why don't you try to be a better girl. I don't want to punish you'.

'But grandfather,' I replied, 'how can I learn so much of that horrid French every day? I'm sure no one else could do it'.

'Hold your tongue, Miss Pert, I must be a better judge than a little girl like you'.

'But, grandfather dear, you know I do love you, and I do try my best'.

'Well, prove your love and diligence in future, or your posterior must feel a nice little birch, I shall get ready for you,' said he sternly.

Another week passed, during which I could not help observing an unusual fire and sparkle in his eyes, whenever I appeared in evening dress at the dinner table (we always dined in quiet state), and he also suggested that I ought to wear a choice little bouquet of fresh flowers in my bosom, to set off my complexion.

But the climax was approaching, I was not to escape long; he again found fault, and gave me what he gravely called one last chance: my eyes were filled with tears, and I trembled to look at his stern old face, and knew any remonstrance on my part would be useless.

The prospect of punishment made me so nervous, it was with the greatest difficulty I could attend to my lessons, and the second day after, I broke down entirely.

'Oh! Ho! it's come to this has it, Rosie?' said the old gentleman, 'nothing will do, you must be punished'.

Ringing the bell for Mrs. Mansell, he told her to have the punishment room and the servants all ready, when he should want them, as he was sorry to say 'Miss Rosa was so idle, and getting worse with her lessons every day, she must now be taken severely in hand or she would be spoiled for life'.

'Now, you bad girl', said he, as the housekeeper retired, 'go to your room and reflect upon what your idleness has brought to you'.

Full of indignation, confusion, and shame, I rushed to my chamber, and bolted the door, determined they should break the door down first before I would submit to such a public exposure, before the two servants; throwing myself on the bed, I gave vent to my tears for at least a couple of hours, expecting every moment the dreadful summons to attend the old man's *punishment drill,* as he called it, but, no one disturbing me, I at last came to the conclusion it was only a plan of his to frighten me, and so I fell into a soothing sleep. A voice at the door awakened me, and I recognized the voice of Jane, as she said, 'Miss Rosa, Miss Rosa, you'll be late for dinner.'

'No dinner for me, Jane, if I'm going to be punished; go away, leave me alone,' whispered I through the keyhole.

'Oh! Miss Rosie, the General's been in the garden all the afternoon, quite good-tempered, perhaps he's forgotten it all; don't make him angry by not being ready for dinner, let me in quick'.

So I cautiously drew the bolt, and let her assist me to dress.

'Cheer up, Miss Rosie, don't look dull, go down as if nothing had happened, and most likely all will be forgotten; his memory is so short, especially if you put in your bosom this sweet little nosegay to please him, as you have never done it since he said it would set off your complexion'.

Thus encouraged, I met my grandfather with a good appetite, and, as if the 'bitterness was past', like Agag before Samuel, little suspecting I should be almost hewed in pieces afterwards.

The dinner passed most pleasantly, for such a formal affair as my grandfather made it, he took several glasses of wine, and in the middle of the dessert seemed to contemplate me with unusual interest; at last suddenly seeming to notice the little bouquet of damask and white roses, he said, 'That's right, Rosa, I see you have carried out my suggestion of a nosegay at last; it quite improves your appearance, but nothing to what my birch will effect on your naughty bottom, which will soon look like one of those fine peaches, and now's the time to do it,' said he, ringing the bell.

Almost distracted, and ready to faint, I rushed for the door, but only in time to fall into the arms of strong Jemima.

'Now for *punishment drill;* march on, Jemima, with the culprit, you've got her safe; Mrs. Mansell and Jane, come on,' said he to them, as they appeared in the background.

Resistance was useless. I was soon carried into a spare room I had never entered; it contained very little furniture, except the carpet, and one comfortable easy chair; but on the walls hung several bunches of twigs, and in one corner stood a thing like a stepladder, but covered with red baize, and fitted with six rings, two halfway up, two at the bottom, and two at the top.

'Tie her to the horse, and get ready for business,' said the General, as he seated himself in the chair, to look on at his ease.

'Come, Rosa, dear, don't be troublesome, and make your grandfather more angry,' said Mrs. Mansell, unfastening my waistband. 'Slip off your dress, whilst the girls put the horse in the middle of the room'.

'Oh! No! No! I won't be whipped,' I screamed. 'Oh! Sir! Oh! Grandfather, do have mercy,' said I, throwing myself on my knees before the old man.

'Come, come, it's no use showing the white feather, Rosa, it's for your own good. No more nonsense. Mrs. Mansell, do your duty, and let us get the painful business over; she isn't one of my stock if she doesn't show her pluck when it comes to the pinch'.

The three women all tried to lift me, but I kicked, scratched, and bit all round, and, for a moment or two, almost beat them off in my fury, but my strength was soon exhausted, and Jemima, smarting from a severe bite, carried me in vengeful triumph to the dreaded machine. Quick as thought, my hands and feet were secured to the upper and lower rings; the horse widening towards the ground caused my legs to be well apart when drawn up closely to the rings at my ankles.

I could hear Sir Eyre chuckle with delight as he exclaimed, 'By God! she's a vixen, and it must be taken out of her, she's a Coote all over. Bravo, Rosie! Now get her ready quickly'.

I submitted in sullen despair, whilst my torn dress and under-skirts were turned up and pinned round my shoulders, but when they began to unloose my drawers, my rage burst out afresh, and turning my head, I saw the old man, his stern face beaming with pleased animation, whisking in his right hand a small bunch of fresh birchen twigs. My blood was in a boil, and my bottom tingled with anticipated strokes, especially when Jemima, pulling the drawers nearly down to my knees, gave me a smart little slap on the sly, to let me know what I might soon expect, and I fairly shouted, 'You must be a cruel old beast to let them treat me so'.

'Old beast, indeed!' said he, jumping up in a passion. 'We'll see about that, Miss; perhaps you'll be glad to apologize before long'.

I saw him stepping forward. 'Oh! Mercy! Mercy! Sir! I didn't mean it; they've hurt me so; I couldn't help what I said'.

'This is a really serious case,' said he, apparently addressing the others. 'She's idle, violently vicious, and even insulting to me, her only natural guardian, instead of treating me with proper respect. There can be no alternative, the only remedy, however painful the scene may be to us who have to inflict the punishment, is to carry it out, as a matter of duty, or the girl will be ruined. She has never been under proper control all her life'.

'Oh! Grandfather, punish me any way but this. I know I can't bear it; it's so dreadfully cruel,' I sobbed out through my tears.

'My child, such crocodile tears have no effect on me; you must be made to feel the smart. If we let you off now, you would be laughing at it all, and go on worse than before. Stand aside, Jane, we can't waste any more time'. So saying, he made a flourish with the rod, so as to make quite an audible 'whisk' in the air. I suppose it was only to clear the way, as it did not touch me; in fact up to this time, he had treated me like a cat which knows the poor mousey cannot escape, but may be pounced upon at any time.

I could see the tears in Jane's eyes, but Jemima had a malicious smile on her face, and Mrs. Mansell looked very grave, but no time was allowed for reflections; the next instant I felt a smart but not heavy stroke right across my loins, then another, and another, in rather quick succession, but not too fast for me to think that perhaps after all it would not be so dreadful as I feared; so setting my teeth firmly without uttering a word, I determined to give as little indica-tion as possible of my feelings. All this and a great deal more flashed through my brain before six strokes had been administered, my bottom tingled all over, and the blood seemed to rush like lightning through my veins at every blow, and my face felt as my poor posteriors.

'Now, you idle puss,' said the General, 'you begin to feel the fruits of your conduct. Will you? Will you call me an old beast again?' giving a harder stroke at each ejaculation.

My courage still sustained my resolution not to cry out, but only seemed to make him more angry.

'Sulky tempered and obstinate, by Jove!' he continued; 'we must draw it out of you. Don't think, Miss, I'm to be beaten by a little wench like you; take that, and that, and that,' whisking me with still greater energy, concluding with a tremendous whack which drew up the skin to bursting tension, and I felt another like it would make the blood spurt forth, but he suddenly paused in his fury, as if for want of breath, but as I now know too well, only to prolong his own exquisite pleasure.

Thinking all was over, I entreated them to let me go, but to my sorrow soon found my mistake.

'Not yet, not yet, you bad girl, you're not half punished for all your biting, scratching, and impudence,' exclaimed Sir Eyre.

Again the hateful birch hissed through the air, and cut into my bruised flesh, both buttocks and thighs, suffering and smarting in agony, but he seemed careful at first not to draw the blood; however, I was not to escape, it was only his deliberate plan of attack, so as not to exhaust the poor victim too soon.

'Bite, and scratch, and fight against my orders again, will you? Miss Rosie, you'll know next time what to expect. You deserve no mercy, the idleness was bad enough, but such murderous conduct is awful; I believe you would have killed anyone in your passion if you could. Bite, scratch, and fight, eh! Bite, will you?' Thus lectured the old man, getting warmer and warmer in his attack, till the blood fairly trickled down my poor thighs.

I was in dreadful agony at every cut, and must have fainted, but his lecturing seemed to sustain me like a cordial; besides, with the pain I experienced a most pleasurable warmth and excitability impossible to be described, but which, doubtless, you, my dear, have felt for yourself when under my discipline.

But all my fortitude could not much longer suppress my sighs and moans, and at last I felt as if I must die under the torture, in spite of the exquisite sensation which mingled with it; notwithstanding my ohs and ahs, and stifled cries, I would not ask for mercy again; my sole thoughts ran upon the desire for vengeance, and how I should like to whip and cut them all in pieces, especially the General and Jemima, and even poor tearful Jane.

Sir Eyre seemed to forget his age, and worked away in frightful excitement.

'Damme, won't you cry for mercy? Won't you apologize, you young hussy,' he hissed between his teeth. 'She's tougher and more obstinate than any of the family, a real chip of the old block. But to be beaten by the young spitfire, Mrs. Mansell, is more than I can bear. There! there! there!' cried he; and at last the worn-out stump of the rod fell from his hand, as he sank back quite exhausted in his chair.

'Mrs. Mansell,' he gasped, 'give her half-a-dozen good stripes with a new rod to finish her off, and let her know that although she may exhaust an old man, there are other strong arms that can dispense justice to her impudent rump'.

The housekeeper, in obedience to the command, takes up a fine fresh birch, and cuts deliberately, counting, in clear voice, one, two, three, four, five, six (her blows were heavy, but did not seem to sting so cruelly as those given by Sir Eyre). 'There,' she says, 'Miss Rosa, I might have laid it on more heavily, but I pitied you this first time'.

Nearly dead, and frightfully cut up, although victorious, I had to be carried to my room. But what a victory! All torn and bleeding, as I was, besides the certainty that the old General would renew his attack at the first favourable opportunity.

Poor Jane laughed and cried over my lacerated posteriors as she tenderly washed me with cold arnica and water, and she seemed so used to the business that when we retired to rest (for I got her to sleep with me) I asked her if she had not often attended bruised bottoms before.

'Yes, Miss Rosie,' she replied; 'but you must keep the secret and not pretend to know anything. I have been whipped myself, but not so bad as you were, although it's cruel. We all rather like it after the first time or two; especially if we are not cut up too much. Next time you should shout out well for mercy, &c., as it pleases the old man, and he won't be so furious. He was so bad and exhausted with whipping you, Mrs. Mansell was going to send for the doctor, but Jemima said a good birching would do him more good, and draw the blood away from his head; so they pickled him finely, till he quite came to himself, and begged hard to be let off'.

Thus ended my first lesson.

My Dear Nellie,

To continue my tale where I left off. Jane and I had some further conversation next morning, which, to the best of my recollection, was as follows:—

ROSA.—'So, Jane, you have been whipped, have you. What was it for?'

JANE.—'The first time was for being seen walking with a young man coming from church. The General said I had never been, and only pretended to be religious for the chance of gadding about with young fellows, which must be checked, or I should be ruined'.

ROSA.—'Well; didn't you feel revengeful at being whipped for that?'

JANE.—'So I did, but forgot all about it in the delight I had in seeing Jemima well cut up. Oh, she did just catch it, I can tell you; but she's as strong and hard as leather'.

ROSA.—'So I could forget and forgive too, if I could but cut you all up well. I've had a good mind to begin with you, Jane, when I don't feel quite so sore'.

JANE.—'Ah! But I know you hate Jemima, and would rather see her triced up to the horse. Perhaps we shall be able to get her into a scrape between us, if we put our heads together'.

ROSA.—'Oh! you sly girl. Don't you think I'll let you off, much as I long to repay the others. Just wait till I feel well enough, and I'll settle you first. There will be plenty of opportunities, as you are to sleep with me in my room every night. I haven't forgotten how you persuaded me to dress for dinner, when you knew, all the time, what was coming'.

JANE.—'Dear Miss Rosie, I couldn't help it. Mrs Mansell sent me up to dress you. The old General put it off till after dinner, as he likes to see the culprits dressed as nicely as possible. If he punished any of us, we have to attend *punishment drill* in our very best clothes, and if they get damaged, Mrs. Mansell soon fits us out again, so we don't lose much by a good birching. I have known

Jemima to get into trouble so as to damage her things, but Sir Eyre made her smart well for them'.

I was very sore for several days, but managed to make and secrete a fine bunch of twigs, ready for Miss Jane when she would little expect it; in fact, she did not know I had been into the garden or out of the house. Of course she was a much stronger and bigger girl than myself, so I should have to secure her by some stratagem. I let her think I had quite forgotten my threat, but one evening, just as we were both undressed for bed, I said, 'Jane, did Mrs. Mansell or Jemima ever birch you without grandfather knowing it?'

JANE.—'Yes, dear Miss Rosie, they've served me out shamefully, more than once'.

ROSA.—'How did they manage that?'

JANE.—'Why, I was tied by my hands to the foot of the bedstead'.

ROSA.—'Oh! Do show me, and let me tie you up to see how it all looked'.

JANE.—'Very well; if it's any pleasure to you, Miss'.

ROSA.—'What shall I tie you up with? You're as strong as Samson'.

JANE.—'A couple of handkerchiefs will do, and there's a small comforter to tie my legs'.

By her directions I soon had her hands tied to the two knobs at the foot of the bed, and her feet stretched out a little behind were secured to the legs of the table.

'Oh! My!' said Jane. 'You have fixed me tight. What did you tie so hard for? I can't get away till you release me'.

'Stay! Stay!' I cried. 'I must see you quite prepared now you are properly fixed up'; and I quickly turned up her nightdress and secured it well above her waist, so as to expose her plump bottom and delicately mossed front to my astonished gaze.

'Oh! What a beauty you are, Jane', said I kissing her, 'and you know I love you, but your naughty little bum-be-dee must be punished. It is a painful duty, but I'll let you see it's no joke, Miss. Look, what a fine swishtail I've got,' producing my rod.

'Mercy! Mercy!' cried Jane. 'Dear Miss Rosie, you won't beat me; I've always been so kind to you!'

'It won't do, Jane, I must do my duty. You were one of the lot against me, and the first I can catch. It may be years before I can pay off the others'.

The sight of her beautiful posteriors filled me with a gloating desire to exercise my skill upon them, and see a little of what I had to feel myself. Nervously grasping my birch, without further delay, I commenced the assault by some sharp strokes, each blow deepening the rosy tints to a deeper red.

'Ah! Ah! What a shame. You're as bad as the old General, you little witch, to take me so by surprise'.

'You don't seem at all sorry, Miss,' I cried; 'But I'll try and bring down your impudence; in fact, I begin to think you are one of the worst of them, and only acted the hypocrite, with your pretended compassions, when you were, in reality, in it all the time. But it's my turn now. Of course, you were too strong for me, unless I had trapped you so nicely. How do you like it, Miss Jane?' All this time I kept on, whisk, whisk, whisk, in quick succession, till her bottom began to look quite interesting.

'You little wretch! You vixen!' gasped Jane. 'Your grandfather shall hear of this'.

'That's your game, is it, Miss Tell-tale. At any rate, you'll be well paid first,' I replied. The sight of her buttocks only seemed to add to my energy, and it was quite a thrill of pleasure when I first saw the blood come. She writhed and wriggled with suppressed sighs and ahs, but each time she gave utterance to any expression, it seemed only for the purpose of irritating me more and more. My excitement became intense, the cruel havoc seemed to be an immense satisfaction to me, and her bottom really was in a deplorable state through my inconsiderate fury. At last, quite worn out and fatigued, I could hold the rod no longer, and my passion melted into love and pity, as I saw her in an apparently listless and fainting condition, with drooping head, eyes closed, and hands clenched.

The worn-out birch was dropped, and kissing her tenderly, I sobbed out, 'Jane, dear, Jane, I both love and forgive you now, and you will find me as tender to you as you were to me after my flogging'.

Her hands and feet were soon released, when to my astonishment, she threw her arms round my neck as with sparkling eyes and a luscious kiss she said softly, 'And I forgive you too, Miss Rosie, for you don't know what pleasure you have given me, the last few moments have been bliss indeed'.

This was all a puzzle to me at the time, but I understood it well enough afterwards. She made quite light of her bruised bottom, saying, 'What was awful to you was nothing to me, Miss Rosie, I am so much older and tougher; besides, the first time is always the worst; it was too bad of Sir Eyre to cut you up as he did, but your obstinacy made him forget himself; you'll grow to like it as I do'.

This and much more in the same strain passed as we bathed and soothed the irritated parts, and we finally fell asleep with a promise from me to let her give me a pleasant lesson in a day or two.

Things went on smoothly for a few days, my punishment had been too severe for me to lightly dare a second engagement with the General; still I burned for a chance to avenge myself on anyone but Jane, who was now my bosom friend. We discussed all sorts of schemes for getting anyone but ourselves into trouble, but to no purpose. The old gentleman often cautioned me to take care, as the next time he should not fail to make me cry, 'Peccavi'.

One fine afternoon, however, being in the garden with the house-keeper, I remarked to her, 'What a pity it was grandfather let the nectarines hang and spoil, and no one allowed to taste them'.

'My dear,' said Mrs. Mansell, 'if you take two or three he'll never miss them, only you must not tell that I said so, it's a shame to let them rot'.

'But, Mrs. Mansell, that would be stealing,' I replied.

'When nothing's lost nothing can have been stolen; it's only a false sense of honesty, and you, the little mistress of the house,' she urged.

'Well, you are the serpent, and I'm Eve, I suppose; they really do look delicious, and you won't tell, will you?' I asked in my simplicity; so the fruit was plucked, and Mrs. Mansell helped to eat it, which put me quite at my ease.

Just before dinner next day we were surprised by the General calling us all into his sitting-room, 'How's this, Mrs. Mansell?' he said, looking fearfully angry, 'I can't leave my keys in the lock of that cabinet without someone tasting my rum; I've long known there was a sly sipping thief about, so I have been sly too. Finding it was the rum that was most approved, the last time the decanter was filled I put a little scratch with my diamond ring, to mark the height of the liquor in the bottle, and have only used the brandy for myself. Look! whoever it is has got through nearly a pint in three or four days. Come here, Rosa, now Mrs. Mansell, and now Jemima,' said he, sternly, smelling the breath of each in turn.

'Woman,' he said, as she faltered and hesitated to undergo this ordeal, 'I didn't think you were a sneaking thief, if you really wanted a little spirit, Mrs. Mansell would have let you have it, I dare say, as you have been with us some years, and we don't like change, but you shall be cured of thieving to-morrow; you should have been well thrashed at once, but we have a friend to dinner this evening, it will do you good to wait and think of what's coming. Be off, now, and mind the dinner's served up properly or you'll catch it in Indian style to-morrow, and be a curried chicken if ever you were'.

Our visitor was an old fox-hunting colonel, our nearest neighbour, and my spirits were so elated at the prospect of Jemima's punishment that it seemed to me the pleasantest evening I had ever spent in that house.

All next day grandfather spent looking over the garden, and a presentiment came over me that the nectarines would be missed; if he had been so cunning in one thing, he might be in another.

My fears were only too well founded, for catching sight of me with the housekeeper, cutting a nosegay for the criminal's wear, he said, 'Mrs. Mansell, you had better make another bouquet whilst you are about it, someone has been at the nectarines; do you know anything about it, Rosa?'

'Oh! Grandfather, you know I was strictly forbidden to touch the fruit,' said I, as innocently as possible.

'Mrs. Mansell, do you know anything of it, as she won't give a direct answer,' said he, eyeing me sternly.

I was covered with confusion, and to make it worse, Mrs. Mansell with affected reluctance to tell an untruth, confessed the whole affair.

'Pon my word, a nice honest lot you all are, as I dare say Jane is like the rest; Mrs. Mansell, I'm astonished at you, and I think your punishment will be enough, when you consider how seriously I look upon such things, but as to that girl Rosa, prevarication is worse than a lie, such cunning in one so young is frightful, but we'll settle Jemima first, and then think of what's to be done'.

Left in this state of uncertainty, I fled to Jane for consolation, who assured me it was a good thing Jemima stood first, as the old man would get exhausted, and perhaps let me off lightly, if I screamed and begged for mercy.

Thus encouraged, I managed to eat a good dinner, and took an extra glass of wine on the sly (I was only supposed to take one).

Thus fortified I marched to the *punishment drill* with great confidence, especially as I so wished to see Jemima well thrashed.

When first I set eyes upon her, as she curtseyed to the General, who was seated in the chair, rod in hand, her appearance struck me with admiration; rather above medium height, dark auburn hair, fresh colour, and sparkling blue eyes, low cut dark blue silk dress, almost revealing the splendours of her full rounded bosom, the large nosegay fixed rather on one side under her dimpled chin, pink satin high-heeled shoes, with silver buckles; she had short sleeves, but fawn-coloured gloves of kid, and a delicate net, covering her arms to the elbows, took off all coarseness of her red skin or hands.

'Prepare her at once,' said the General, 'she knows too well all I would say. Here, Rosie, hand me down that big bunch of birch, this little one is no use for her fat rump. Ha! ha! this is better,' said he, whisking it about.

Jane and the housekeeper had already stripped off the blue silk, and were proceeding to remove the underskirts of white linen, trimmed with broad lace; the bouquet had fallen to the floor, and presently the submissive victim stood with only chemise and drawers. What a glimpse I had of her splendid white neck and bosom, what deliciously full and rounded legs, with pink silk stockings and handsome garters (for the General was very strict as to the costume of his penitents).

I assisted to tie her up, and unfastening her drawers, Jane drew them well down, whilst Mrs Mansell pinned up her chemise, fully exposing the broad expanse of her glorious buttocks, the brilliant whiteness of her skin showing to perfection by the dazzling glare of the well-lighted room. I gave her two or three smart pats of approval just to let her know I hadn't forgotten the slap she gave me, then drew aside to make way for Sir Eyre.

My thoughts were so entirely absorbed by the fascinating spectacle that I lost all remembrance of my own impending turn. Whack! came the big birch, with a force to have made her jump out of her skin, if possible, but only a stifled, 'Ah—r—r—re!' and a broad, red mark were the results; the blood mounted to her face, and she seemed to hold her breath for each blow as it came, but the rod was so heavy, and the old General so vigorous, that in less than a dozen strokes her fair bottom was smeared with blood and bits of birch were lying in all directions. 'Ah! Ah!! Oh!!!' she screamed, 'do have mercy, sir, I can't stand it. Oh! oh! indeed I can't'.

'You sly thief, don't think I'll let you off before you're dead; if I don't cure you now I shall lose a good servant,' exclaimed Sir Eyre, cutting away.

My blood boiled with excitement of a most pleasurable kind, young as I was, and cruel as I knew it to be, no pity for the victim entered my breast; it is a sensation only to be experienced by real lovers of the rod.

'You like rum, do you, Miss?' said the General. 'Did you take it raw or mixed? I'll make your bottom raw'.

The poor old man was obliged now to sit down for want of breath. Mrs. Mansell, understanding his wishes, at once took his place with a fresh birch, without giving the victim any respite.

'She must, indeed, be well punished, sir. I'm sure they're never denied anything so long as they behave themselves,' said she, with a stern relentless face; in fact, after a stroke or two, her light-brown hair was all in disorder from the exertion, and her dashing hazel eyes, and well-turned figure, made me think her a goddess of vengeance. 'Will you? Will you do so again? You ungrateful thief,' she kept on saying, with a blow to each question.

Poor Jemima moaned, sobbed, and sometimes cried out for mercy, whilst the blood fairly trickled down her thighs, but the housekeeper seemed to hear nothing, and Sir Eyre was in an ecstasy of gloating delight. This could not last long, however, strong the victim might be. Becoming exhausted with her accumulated sensations, she at last fairly fainted, and we had to dash cold water over her face to recover her; then covered with a cloak, she was led off to her room, and left to herself.

'Now, Rosa,' said the General, holding out a light green bunch of fresh birch, 'kiss the rod, and get ready for your turn'.

Hardly knowing what I was about, I inclined my head and gave the required kiss. Mrs. Mansell and Jane had me prepared in no time, as I was quite passive; and as soon as I was fairly exposed and spread-eagled on the horse, the old General rose to his task.

'You have seen how severe I can be, by Jemima's punishment,' said he; 'but, perhaps, you did not think your answer to me yesterday was any offense, and I am almost inclined to forgive you, but remember in future, if you get off lightly this time, a plain lie is better than prevarication. I think the last flogging must have done you great good, your conduct is quite different to-night. But now, remember—remember—remember!' he cried again, giving sharp, cutting strokes at each word. My poor bottom tingled with agony, and I cried loudly for mercy, promising to be strictly truthful in future; so, after about twenty strokes, he said: 'You may go this time,' finishing me off with a tremendous remembrance, which made me fairly shake with the concussion, and was the only blow which actually drew the blood, although I had some fine tender weals.

Your loving friend
Rosa Belinda Coote.

LADY POKINGHAM; OR THEY ALL DO IT:

Giving an Account of her Luxurious Adventures, both before and after her Marriage with Lord Crim-Con.

INTRODUCTION

To the Reader,

Very little apology will be needed for putting in print the following highly erotic and racy narrative of a young patrician lady, whose adventures I feel assured every genuine lover of voluptuous reading will derive as much or more pleasure afforded your humble servant.

The subject of these memoirs was one of the brightest and most charming of her sex, endued with such exquisite nervous sensitiveness, in addition to an unusual warmth of constitution, that she was quite unable to resist the seductive influences of God's finest creation; for God made man in his own image, male and female, created he them; and this was the first commandment, 'Be faithful and multiply, and replenish the earth'—see Genesis, chap. 1.

The natural instinct of the ancients instilled in their minds the idea that copulation was the direct and most acceptable form of worship they could offer to their deities, and I know that those of my readers who are not bigoted Christians will agree with me, that there cannot be any great sin in giving way to natural desires, and enjoying, to the utmost, all those delicious sensations for which a beneficent Creator has so amply fitted us.

Poor girl, she did not live long, and in thoroughly enjoying her few brief years of butterfly life, who can think her wicked!

The scraps from which my narrative is compiled were found in a packet she had entrusted to a devoted servitor, who, after her sudden and premature death at the early age of twenty-three, entered my service.

As author, I feel the crudeness of my style may be a little offensive to some, but hope my desire to afford general pleasure will excuse my defects.

THE AUTHOR

PART I

My dear Walter,

How I love you! but alas! you will never know it till I am gone; little do you think, as you wheel me about in my invalid chair, how your delicate attentions have won the heart of a poor consumptive on the verge of the grave. How I long to suck the sweets of love from your lips; to fondle and caress your lordly priapus, and feel its thrilling motions within me; but such joys cannot be, the least excitement would be my death, and I can but sigh as I look at your kind loving face, and admire the fine proportions of my darling, as evidenced by the large bunch of keys you always seem to have in your pocket; indeed you look to have a key of keys, whose burning thrust would unlock any virgin cabinet.

This is a strange fancy of mine (the writing for your perusal a short account of some of my adventures); but one of the only pleasures left me is to indulge in reveries of the past, and seem to feel over again the thrilling emotions of voluptuous enjoyments, which are now denied to me; and I hope the recital of my escapades and follies may afford you some slight pleasure, and add to the lasting regard with which I hope you will remember me in years to come. One thing I ask of you, dear Walter, is to fancy you are enjoying Beatrice Pokingham when you are in the embraces of some future inamorata. It is a pleasure I have often indulged in myself when in the action of coition, and heightened my bliss by letting my fancy run riot, and imagined I was in the arms of someone I particularly wished for, but could not come at. My income dies with me, so I have no cause to make a will, but you will find notes for a few hundred pounds enclosed with this outline of my adventures, which is all I have been able to save. You will also find a fine lock of dark brown hair, which I have cut from the abundant chevelure of my Mons Veneris; other friends and relatives may have the admired curls from my head, your memento is cut from the sacred spot of love.

I never remember my father, the Marquis of Pokingham, but have my doubts as to whether I am really entitled to the honour of claiming him as a parent, as he was a used-up old man, and from papers and letters, which passed privately between him and my mother, I know that he more than suspected he was indebted to his good-looking footman for the pretty baby girl my mother presented to him; as he says in one note, 'that he could have forgiven every-thing if the fruits of her intercourse with James had been a son and heir, so as to keep his hated nephew out of the estates and title, and wished her to let him cultivate her parsley bed for another crop, which might perhaps turn out more in accordance with his wishes'. The poor old fellow died soon after writing that note, and my mother, from whom this dreadful consumption is transmitted to me, also left me an orphan at an early age, leaving me her jointure of £20,000, and an aristocratic title which that amount was quite inadequate to properly support.

My guardians were very saving and careful, as they sent me to school at eight years of age, and only spent about £150 a year for schooling and necessaries, till they thought it was time for me to be brought out in the world, so that I benefitted considerably by the accumulated interest of my money.

The first four years of my school passed away uneventfully, and during that time I was only in one serious scrape, which I will relate, as it led to my first taste of a good birch rod.

Miss Birch was rather an indulgent schoolmistress, and only had to resort to personal punishment for very serious offences, which she considered might materially affect the future character of her pupils, unless thoroughly cut out of them from the first. I was nearly seven years old when I had a sudden fancy for making sketches on my slate in school. One of our governesses, Miss Pennington, was a rather crabbed and severe old girl of five-and-thirty, and particu-larly evoked my abilities as a caricaturist, and the sketches would be slyly passed from one to the other of us, causing considerable giggling and gross inattention to our lessons. I was infatuated and conceited with what I considered my clever drawings and several admonitions and extra tasks as punishment had no effect in checking

C

my mischievous interruptions, until one afternoon Miss Birch had fallen asleep at her desk, and old Penn was busy with a class, when the sudden inspiration seized me to make a couple of very rude sketches; one of the old girl sitting on a chamber utensil; but the other was a rural idea of her stooping down, with her clothes up to ease herself, in a field. The first girl I showed them to almost burst with laughter, and two others were so anxious to see the cause of her mirth, that they were actually stooping over her shoulder to look at my slate, when, before I could possibly get to it to rub them off, old Penn pounced upon it like an eagle, and carried it in triumph to Miss Birch, who was awakened, chagrined by the amused smile which our principal could not repress at first sight of the indecent caricatures.

'My young lady must smart for this, Miss Pennington,' said Miss Birch, with suddenly assumed gravity; 'she has been very troublesome lately with these impudent drawings, but this is positively obscene; if she draws one thing she will go to another. Send for Susan to bring my birch rod! I must punish her whilst my blood is warm, as I am too forgiving, and may let her off'.

I threw myself on my knees, and implored for mercy, promising 'Never, never to do anything of the kind again'.

MISS BIRCH.—'You should have thought of the consequences before you drew such filthy pictures; the very idea of one of my young ladies being capable of such productions is horrible to me; these prurient ideas cannot be allowed to settle in your mind for an instant, if I can whip them out'.

Miss Pennington, with a grim look of satisfaction, now took me by the wrist, just as Susan, a stout, strong, fair servant girl of about twenty, appeared with what looked to me a fearful big bunch of birch twigs, neatly tied up with red velvet ribbon.

'Now, Lady Beatrice Pokingham,' said Miss Birch, 'kneel down, confess your fault, and kiss the rod,' taking the bunch from Susan's hands, and extending it to me as a queen might her sceptre to a supplicant subject.

Anxious to get over the inevitable, and make my punishment as light as possible, I knelt down, and with real tears of penitence begged her to be as lenient as her sense of justice would admit, as I knew I well deserved what she was going to inflict, and would take care not to insult Miss Pennington again, whom I was very sorry to have caricatured; then I kissed the rod and resigned myself to my fate.

MISS PENNINGTON, maliciously.—'Ah! Miss Birch, how quickly the sight of the rod makes hypocritical repentance'.

MISS BIRCH.—'I quite understand all that, Miss Pennington, but must temper justice with mercy at the proper time; now, you impudent artist, lift your clothes behind, and expose your own bottom to the justly merited punishment'.

With trembling hands I lifted my skirts, and was then ordered to open my drawers also; which done, they pinned up my dress and petticoats as high as my shoulders; then I was laid across a desk, and Susan stood in front of me, holding both hands, whilst old Penn and the French governess (who had just entered the schoolroom) each held one of my legs, so that I was what you might call help-lessly spread-eagled.

MISS BIRCH, looking seriously round as she flourished the rod.— 'Now, all you young ladies, let this whipping be a caution to you; my Lady Beatrice richly deserves this degrading shame, for her indecent (I ought to call them obscene) sketches. Will you! will you, you troublesome, impudent little thing, ever do so again? There, there, there, I hope it will soon do you good. Ah! you may scream; there's a few more to come yet'.

The bunch of birch seemed to crash on my bare bottom with awful force; the tender skin smarted, and seemed ready to burst at every fresh cut. 'Ah! ah! oh!!! Oh, heavens! have mercy, madame. Oh! I will never do anything like it again. Ah—r—re! I can't bear it!' I screamed, kicking and struggling under every blow, so that at first they could scarcely hold me, but I was soon exhausted by my own efforts.

MISS BIRCH.—'You can feel it a little, may it do you good, you bad little girl; if I don't check you now, the whole establishment would soon be demoralized. Ah! ha! your bottom is getting finely wealed, but I haven't done yet,' cutting away with increasing fury.

Just then I caught a glimpse of her face, which was usually pale, but now flushed with excitement, and her eyes sparkled with un-wonted animation. 'Ah!' she continued, 'young ladies beware of my rod, when I do have to use it. How do you like it, Lady Beatrice? Let us all know how nice it is,' cutting my bottom and thighs deliberately at each ejaculation.

LADY BEATRICE.—'Ah! oh! ah—r—r—re! It's awful! Oh, I shall

die if you don't have mercy, Miss Birch. Oh! my God, I'm fearfully punished; I'm cut to pieces; the birch feels as if it was red hot, the blows burn so!'

Then I felt as if it was all over, and I must die soon; my cries were succeeded by low sobs, moans, and then hysterical crying, which gradually got lower and lower, till at last I must have fainted, as I remembered nothing more till I found myself in bed, and awoke with my poor posteriors tremendously bruised and sore, and it was nearly a fortnight before I got rid of all the marks of that severe whipping.

A COPY OF A LETTER

Was given mee by my cozen SC of Kempston, and written in a Tarpaulin style.

Madame,—

Premising you are safe returned to Towne, I made bold to acquaint you that Mr. F—is lately arriv'd att ye haven of Matrimony; He had been long in ye middle state of Purgatory between ye Church & ye Ladyes Chamber; ere she with ye advice of her mother, & some other experienced Ladyes, was lanced forth into ye marriage bed. The Vessell had been 14 years & three months on Building, that it is thought she will care well under Sail. It is a fine smooth ship, I will promise you, & one of ye first-rate; and likely to doe ye King good Service if ably & well man'd. The only fault there is (if any) she is too narrow in ye Poope. She hath a fine shroud, & all difficulty soone vanish'd saving only ye maine yard may prove too burly for the midle Deck. The Capt. it is thought this night will goe on board of her; hee is bound for ye Straites Mouth, and cannot come off without bloodshed: Nay worse; 'tis fear'd if opposition be made, hee may be forced to spend his provision in ye channel, & soe returne without doeing ye Kingdome a penny worth of service.

THE PLEASURES OF LOVE

Pressed in the arms of him I so adored,
The keeper of my charms, my pride, my lord!

By day experiencing each sweet delight,
And meeting endless transports every night.
When on our downy bed we fondly lay,
Heating each other by our am'rous play;
Till Nature, yielding to the luscious game,
Would fierce desire and quenchless lust inflame!
Oh! then we join'd in love's most warm embrace,
And pressed soft kisses on our every grace!
Around my form his pliant limbs entwined,
Love's seat of bliss to him I then resigned!
We pant, we throb, we both convulsive start!
Heavens! then what passions thro' our fibres dart!
We heave, we wriggle, bite, laugh, tremble, sigh!
We taste Elysian bliss—we fondle—die.

THE MEETING OF THE WATERS

A Parody on Moore's Melody

There is not in this wide world a valley so sweet,
As that vale where the thighs of a pretty girl meet:
Oh, the last ray of feeling and life must depart,
Ere the bloom of that valley shall fade from my heart.

Yet it is not that Nature has shed o'er the scene,
The purest of red, the most delicate skin,
'Tis not the sweet smell of the genial hill;
Ah, no! it is something more exquisite still.

'Tis because the last favours of woman are there,
Which make every part of her body more dear.
We feel how the charms of Nature improve,
When we bathe in the spendings of her whom we love.

THE WISE LOVER

Woman and man whene'er inclined,
In mutual goodness pleasure find,

37

The lawful spouse 'tis sweet to embrace,
In hopes to see a lengthen'd race,
      But let who will the truth contest,
      Another's wife is still the best.

When I was young and slightly skill'd,
In blisses womankind can yield,
I lov'd the maid, I lov'd the piece;
But as my wit and years increase,
      I own the sweetest sport in life,
      Is to enjoy your neighbour's wife.

A virgin coy with sidelong eye,
Your mere approach, at once will fly,
Abhors your nasty hot desires,
Nought less than marriage she requires,
      Such maidenheads the wise detest,
      The adultery maidenhead's the best.

The vagrant nymph who sells her charms,
And fills in turn a thousand arms,
Besides the loss of gold and fame,
May set Priapus in a flame,
      Such fire-tailed comets God confound.
      A wife is always safe and sound.

The genial flame I've oft allayed,
With buxom Kate, my chambermaid,
And dozens such as her, but found
Such sport with ills beset around;
      He who at liberty would feast,
      Will find another's wife the best.

A mistress kept at first is sweet,
And joys to do the merry feat;
But bastards come, and hundreds gone,
You'll wish you'd left her charms alone;
      Such breeding hussy's are a pest,
      A neighbour's wife is far the best.

If you are rash, a wife at first
May into horrid fury burst,

'Sir, you shall rue throughout your life
The day you've kissed another's wife'.
      Reply, 'My dear, this gives the zest,
      I always like my neighbour's best'.

Jove, I remember, when inclined
To feast himself on womankind,
Though maids enough to him were free,
Always preferr'd adultery;
      He took the shape of bird and beast,
      To prove Adultery the best.

But while this naughty sport we sing,
Who can forget our gracious King (Geo. IV);
Him many a lady pleasures gives,
For which her husband pay receives,
      God bless King George! His Majesty
      Is patron of Adultery.

I own the dangers of the suit,
The sweetest is forbidden fruit,
And laws as thick as hairs are set,
Around the center of delight;
      This peril gives the highest zest,
      And guarded hoard is sure the best.

The wandering nymph your purse desires,
The chambermaid to rank aspires;
Your wife content with marriage dues,
All further license will refuse;
      He who has put them to the test,
      Must own his neighbour's wife's the best.

FIRST RONDEAU

Ten years ago, on Christmas day,
Fair Helen stole my heart away,
I went to church—but not to pray,
      Ten years ago.

To pray? Yes—pray to Helen's eyes;
Ah! would that we had been more wise;
To-day, she would not recognize
Him, whom she kissed in ecstasies,
    Ten years ago.

SECOND RONDEAU

Again we've met, and now I find,
Her still more luscious to my mind;
She was not to such pranks inclined,
    Ten years ago.

Though now a second time she's wed,
Hers is a most lascivious bed;
Though thirty years she now has sped,
She fucks still better than she did,
    Ten years ago.

LINES WRITTEN UNDER HER PORTRAIT

Such Helen was! religious, young and fair;
A faithful spouse, and blest with babies dear;
But in the church, while week by week she prayed,
An amorous noble long her charms surveyed;
Sunday by Sunday, seated near her pew,
He kept the goddess of his heart in view;
And when the Tenth Commandment was duly read,
'I covet thee,' his burning glances said—
Her humble rank forbade acquaintance free,
Yet high enough it was to guard her modesty;
Her husband was a gamester fierce and rude,
He fled the town, and other loves pursu'd;
She on her jointure fair remained at home,
Close guarded by his mother and her own;
Two months at church, she stood the siege of sighs,
Silence, that spoke, and eloquence of eyes;
Could virtue longer last? at length she fell;
No more, no more, can happy lovers tell.
And mark the sequel! rashly she had sworn
She ne'er would to her faithless lord return;

Her prudent lover urged a course more wise,
His vigour had more force than his advice;
She would not listen, till her swelling zone,
Proved his kind counsel wiser than her own.
Just at that juncture her good man returned,
In time to adopt the babe, that proves him horn'd;
The wedding ring upon her hand you see
Is not her wedding ring, 'twas given by me;
The one her husband gave her, here, behold!
Around my finger wreaths its hallow'd gold;
Her diamond brooch and clasps all brightly shine,
His gifts indeed! the locks they hold are mine;
Far, far away, I now her absence mourn,
Grant me, O Venus! grant a quick return;
Keep Helen virtuous, till again we meet,
And revel in the bliss so naughty and so sweet.

TEMPTATION

Papa and Mamma, Arabella and I,
    Were sitting at supper with nobody by;
Now because they believe me a cozy old fellow,
    They want to induce me to wed Arabella.

I like the girl well, but I don't choose to wed,
    Fair Bella perceives I'm not easily led;
But while Papa told me some prosy old fable,
    She was scratching her marrowbones under the table.

She look'd in my face, and on our eyes catching,
    I just turn'd my head to see what she was scratching;
She had got her right ankle upon her left knee,
    Up to her left garter I fairly could see.

She look'd in my face without shame or aversion.
    While scratching her nakedness for my diversion;
While I sat electrify'd stuck like a fool,
    She put down her petticoats easy and cool.

And ten minutes after she did it again,
   Though knowing I look'd and saw it quite plain;
Come—there was a prank for a delicate virgin,
   Who thought an old bachelor wanting some urging!

A BLACK JOSEPH

[The Trial of Mrs. Inglefield, wife of J. R. Nicholson Inglefield, Esq., Captain of Her Majesty's Ship Scipio, for Adultery with John Webb, a black servant, in the Consistory Court, 1786.]

John Webb—a second Joseph—a black footman to Captain Inglefield, was the only material evidence against the lady. Previous to his deposition he had lived with the parties two years, mostly at Singlewell, a small village near Gravesend. When he first went there, the family consisted of three small children, all girls; in two or three months afterwards his mistress was delivered of a boy.

From the first moment of his being engaged he thought she took more notice of him than became her. She frequently smiled on him and took hold of his hand, and gently pressed it. About a month after her accouchement, happening to be alone with his lady, she put her hand about his neck, and kissed him. Upon the black drawing off, she laughed at him.

The next day after this occurrence, as he was dressing her hair, she put her hand under his apron, and unbuttoned one of the flaps of his breeches, and began handling and playing with his privities, but the witness, not liking this, declared he would not finish her hair if she did not let him alone. The lady, therefore, was again obliged to laugh it off.

The next day after this, in the forenoon, being summoned by the sound of the chamber bell, he went into the room, where he found his mistress alone, sitting on the foot of the bed. Mungo—according to his own account—avoided going near her as much as possible, but at length she caught him by the skirt of his coat, placed him on her lap, and handled his privities on the outside of his breeches, at the same time asking him—'Can you do anything? Do not be afraid; your master will know nothing about it'. All this, however, made no impression on the generative powers of our African hero. He was a eunuch in spirit, though not in parts, and he tore himself away, but whether at this period he left his mistress laughing or crying does not appear.

The succeeding day, however, Mrs. I. renewed the glorious strife; while under the operation of hair-dressing, she once more applied her delicate hand to the rude parts of Master Comb, and was proceeding to unbutton when he drew himself off, leaving his mistress laughing out an intimation that she should leave her bedroom door open that night, and that he must come.

Master Webb, failing to improve the hint, was the next day met in an angry mood by his enraged mistress, who now spoke very harshly to him.

During these attempts it seems the Captain was from home, which was the time, he says, when his mistress tormented him the most. But what affected him more than all was that one day she absolutely kissed him before her daughter, a child of about four years old.

Towards the end of the summer the Captain and his lady resided on board the Scipio, then laying at Scheerness, for about a month, and one morning about 10 o'clock, when they had been there a fortnight, the Captain being gone on shore, his mistress called him into the after-cabin of the ship, and told him to empty a basin of water, which, when he had done, she shut the cabin door, took him round the waist with both her arms, kissed him and then, as a matter of course, handled him about his privities on the outside, he preventing her from unbuttoning.

All these warm attacks our youthful Negro of nineteen manfully withstood, and after some struggling he liberated his sweet desirable person from the fangs of his mistress, but passing from the room he was observed by Charles McCarthy, the steward of the ship, who questioned him as to what he had been doing, to which he replied—'nothing'.

Two or three days after this aquatic adventure, he was questioned by his master as to all the previous particulars, when, like a faithful servant, he told him all that he knew. In consequence of which Captain Inglefield from that time ceased to cohabit with his wife. The concluding declaration of Webb is: 'That he and his mistress, notwithstanding the critical situations in which he was placed, never had once the carnal use and knowledge of each other's bodies'.

McCarthy, the Steward, corroborated the cabin incident, but in the end the Judge declared there was no proof of the lady's guilt, and ordered Captain Inglefield to take his wife home and treat her with matrimonial affection, and to certify his having so done by the first session of the next term.

CO-OPERATIVE PRINCIPLES

It has been suggested to the Editor of THE PEARL that there is a great necessity for a club where gentlemen might get their greens much cheaper and better than at present.

Women are so dear, and at the same time so deceptive in appearance, that one often pays heavily and yet only gets a stinking article for his generous outlay.

To obviate this, it is proposed to start a club, where at least twenty pretty governesses would be engaged at salaries of £100 per annum; there would be French, English, German, Russian, Italian, and even Zulu and Hottentots, so as to assimilate to every variety of taste. These ladies would accommodate the members whenever they might visit the club, and everything in the shape of dress and generous living and indulgence would be extended to these houris, to make them as agreeable as possible, and happy and contented with their fucktious situations.

Gentlemen members would have to pay a subscription of £1 per week, wines and refreshments of course being extra, but supplied at the lowest possible prices compatible with economy and efficiency.

Gentlemen desirous of submitting their names for admission as members, should do so at once to the Editor, Pearl Office, Cock Lane, London, E. C., as the number will be strictly limited to one hundred.

BEFORE

Thou heavenly sun whose golden light
Displays the hills with verdure bright;
Sink thee, oh sink thee, in the west,
And bring the hour I love best.
      This evening shall my bosom prove,
      The richest ecstacies of love.

Soon as thy glorious light retires,
I look for her my heart admires;
A matron she of sober grace,
With wisdom printed on her face.
      This evening shall my bosom prove,
      The richest ecstasies of love.

And is my heart then grown so cold,
As to be pleased with matrons old;
When I might feast on younger things,
Ah, no! a lovely girl she brings!
      This evening shall my bosom prove,
      The richest ecstasies of love.

To war her soldier son has hied,
She offers me his blooming bride;
And if the girl my taste should please,
Her husband I advance with ease.
      This evening shall my bosom prove,
      The richest ecstasies of love.

She tells me of her daughter's form,
Her swelling bubbies ripe and warm,
Her rosy cheeks, her sapphire eyes,
The jutting fullness of her thighs.
      This evening shall my bosom prove,
      The richest ecstasies of love.

Her little mouth, her snowy skin,
The other mouth her smock within;
The more I questioned, more she told,
In thought the darling I behold.
      This evening shall my bosom prove,
      The richest ecstasies of love.

The stirring raptures of her tale,
Made beauty over age prevail;
At length, with many a 'Fie! for shame!'
She quenched for once my raging flame.
        This evening shall my bosom prove,
        The richest ecstasies of love.

And said I that the dame was old,
And thought I that my heart was cold!
Her vigorous limbs are firm and fresh,
And rich she blooms in prime of flesh.
        This evening shall my bosom prove,
        The richest ecstasies of love.

And if the daughter brings the gust,
Of youth to aid the mother's lust;
And plays the game as well as she,
She must a perfect angel be.
        This evening shall my bosom prove,
        The richest ecstasies of love.

PLEASURES OF MEMORY

Sweet is the memory of the scenes
   In boyhood I enjoyed,
Hot vigour thrilling in my veins,
   By no fruition cloy'd.

So innocent a child I seem'd
   That Catherine, Jane, Eliza,
Would treat me as a girl, nor dream'd
   That I was e'er the wiser.

I many a naked frolic spied,
   Nor seem'd a whit to care,
With changeless glance serene I eyed
   Their sexual members bare.

All fear'd the strict severities
   Of Mistress and of Master,
Who thought to crush propensities
   That only throve the faster.

But when I was thirteen I grew
    Too big a boy for this,
The girls grew timid—well they knew
    I might do more than kiss.

No longer Jane would offer me
    The clean shirt nice and warm,
And turn me up and cuddle me,
    Without supposing harm.

And Catherine never called me now
    The bathroom door to keep,
The while she bathed, lest any came
    And say, 'You must not peep'.

Nor Harriet, when she climb'd the trees,
    Would let me now stand under,
All seem'd to guard their modesties
    With care that made me wonder.

But fostering Venus kindly led
    Her young disciple still,
Although I kept my maidenhead
    Sorely against my will.

For though from British blood I sprung
    Yet born in India's land,
I felt while callow, raw and young
    Cythera's guiding hand.

And night by night, when fast asleep,
    Wits, nerves upon the stretch,
My melting heart I could not keep,
    I was an amorous wretch.

One day I chanced to climb outside
    My cousin's bathing room,
And found a hole through which I spied
    The place I'd used to roam.

I sigh'd to think how oft the girls
    Had idly let me in,
'It's nobody but little Charles,
    No matter though he's seen'.

Yes, I was their sole favourite,
  No other boy was suffer'd
To share in many a luscious sight
  To me so freely offer'd.

'Those joys (thought I) are now no more!'
  I started—at that minute,
Dear Kate came to the bathroom door,
  She lock'd herself within it.

'Oh, do I dream, or is it true?
  And is she going to bathe,
And treat me to the fullest view
  Of all above, beneath?'

She dropt her gown, and one by one
  She stript her of her clothes,
Her smock is all she now has on,
  'Oh, will she nought expose?'

There, now it's off—and Catherine stands
  In utter nudity,
And neither of her rosy hands
  Conceals her modesty.

I saw her right before my eyes
  Naked, stark naked stand,
The blooming centre of her thighs
  As naked as my hand.

What see I now! what see I not!
  Is Kate a woman grown?
She was a little girl I thought,
  But lo, she's fully blown:

Oh look at her sweet *fie for shame*,
  With pouting lips so red.
Oh look at her dear frisky game,
  Her open maidenhead!

The Lady Freemason

Strictly private, except to Brothers,

By Order

THE LADY FREEMASON

As a brother of old, from his lodge was returning,
He called on his sweetheart, with love he was burning,
He wanted some *favours*, says she, 'Not so free,'
Unless you reveal your *famed* secrets to me'.

'Agreed—'tis a bargain—you must be prepared,
Your legs well exposed, your bosom all bared'.
Then hoodwinked and silent, says she, 'I'll be mum,
In despite of the poker you'll clap on my bum'.

To a chamber convenient his fair charge he bore,
Placed her in *due form*, having *closed tight* the door,
Then presented the point of his sharp *Instrumentis*,
And the Lady was soon made an 'entered apprentice'.

His working tools next to her gaze he presented,
To improve by them seriously she then consented,
And *handled* his *jewels* his *gavel* and *shaft*,
That she in a jiffey was passed 'fellow craft'.

She next wanted *raising*, says he, 'There's no urgency,'
She pleaded that this was a *case of emergency*,
His *column* looked to her in no particular way,
But she very soon made it assume perpendicular.

He used all his efforts to raise the young elf,
But found he required much raising himself;
The task was beyond him. Oh! shame and disaster,
He broke down in his *charge*, and she became *master*.

Exhausted and faint, still no rest could betide him,
For she like a glutton soon mounted astride him,
'*From refreshment to labour*,' says he, 'let us march.
Says he, 'You're exalted—you are now *royal arch*'.

In her zeal for true knowledge, no labour, no shirking,
His *jewels* and *furniture* constantly working,
By night and by day, in the light of the dark,
With *pleasure* her lover she guides to the *mark*.

49

D

AN ADVENTURE WITH A TRIBADE;

*Related in a Letter From a Young Lady
to Her Sister*

The next day at dinner time the impatient Caroline came herself to fetch me. As soon as we were in the carriage, she gave loose to her joy; she looked at me, embraced, and pressed me in her arms, never had I inspired more lively transports.

When we arrived she introduced me into the saloon, but this place not being convenient she was obliged to constrain herself rather more. After half an hour's animated conversation, in which she convinced me that she was not less well-informed than singular, dinner was announced. Placing ourselves at table she appeared almost instantaneously to abandon the reserve she had imposed on herself in the saloon. I never partook of a more delicious repast, the meats were exquisite, and the wines like nectar. Caroline helped me abundantly, pressing me to empty my glass by invitation as well as example, whilst a perfect harmony of celestial music poured in a flood through the perfumed air, which was fragrant with all the perfumes of Arabia; every moment she committed fresh thefts; the most passionate lover could not have attached more value to such insignificant trifles.

We were only waited on by two young girls, extremely pretty, and who were doubtless initiated in the sweet pleasures of their mistress, for their presence did not prevent her lavishing on me the most tender caresses. The diversity of wines and liqueurs which I had been forced to drink, that delicious harmony whose varied modulations alternately inspired the most lively transports and the most voluptuous languor, the advances of Caroline, her free discourse; all, in short, contributed to make me share her delirium, so that when she passed from the table to the boudoir, not only her sex was no longer an obstacle to my impetuous desires, but the novelty of that piquante and singular scene seemed to add to their intensity.

The most exquisite perfumes were burning at the feet of the principal statue.

'Do you see,' said Caroline, regarding it, her cheeks on fire, 'do you see with what greedy curiosity Venus examines the charms of Algae, the most beautiful of the graces? The marble seems to

50

become animated at the sight of such attractions. Ah, my Julia, let me imitate it; let my hands, my eyes, do so also. But let us divest ourselves of these inconvenient robes, let there be no obstacles to our burning transports, every veil which covers you robs me of a pleasure!'

In a moment Caroline reduced me to a state of pure nature; far from resisting, I imitated her eagerness; the new beauties which discovered themselves to our view extorted a cry of admiration, and suspended our burning caresses.

Our hands, which for an instant seemed to have respected so many charms, wander with fresh delirium. Caroline takes me in her arms, drags me on to the ottoman, and obliges me to assume the attitude of Algae! I recline with my head resting on one of my arms, the right foot on the ottoman, the knee raised, whilst the left leg, unsupported, gently balances itself.

My *chère amie*, not less curious than Venus, takes the same posture, and places herself exactly in front of the throne of felicity, one of the beautiful knees rests on a cushion, the other serves for a footstool. Caroline, at her ease, contemplates the object of her dearest desires. Her delicate hand opens the rose, and the new Sappho exclaims with transports of joy, impossible to describe, 'She is still a virgin! Good God, what a source of pleasure!'

I confess I could never have imagined this discovery of such great value to her; virgin or not, what need she care? But we cannot account for the eccentricity of the passions, and doubtless the most singular of all is to find one female amorous of another.

Love! thou who inflamed Caroline with the most ardent fires for one of her own sex, lend me thy burning pencil that I may worthily describe this voluptuous scene, as even in forcing us to give way to thy caprices, thy only object is to render us happy!

Caroline rises transported, presses me in her arms, giving a thousand kisses, then resuming her first attitude, contemplates anew the prettiest of bijous. 'Yes,' she exclaims, 'that flower is untouched. What colour! What freshness! Similar to the bee, I will extract the ambrosia! I will intoxicate myself with its delicious juice. I will drain it with pleasure!'

Then by a thousand means, which I dare not describe, but which occasioned me the most delicious sensations, Caroline made me attain the last period of delight. Her design was not merely to procure me delight; the skilful bee, wanting in the natural engine necessary to extract the honey from the rose, made use of her lascivious tongue to draw down my ambrosial tribute to love, titillating and sucking in such a rapturous manner that her face was almost drowned by my impetuous emission, as I went off into a most delicious state of almost unconscious lethargy.

Expressions would vainly endeavour to give an idea of Caroline's excitement; she seemed to have lost her reason as the source of life, her words were as incoherent as her conduct was extravagant. But what do I say? Was she not more sensible than ever, since all she said, everything she did, only tended to increase our intoxication, and add to its fury. Caroline, whose desires no longer knew any restraints, in order to satisfy them, made me pass through all the gradations of pleasure. I tasted in the same evening all those indescribable enjoyments which I should not have been acquainted with until after a long novitiate, had not the extraordinary passion I inspired her with induced her to initiate me at once in the most secret mysteries.

What charming pictures could I describe were I permitted to give the reins to my pen.

My imagination, exalted by these enchanting souvenirs, longs to retrace the image! But, alas! I must confine in my bosom the secret ready to escape, and deprive the most beautiful half of the human race of a fruitful source of pleasures and voluptuousness, of which the experience alone can conceive the extent!

SALLY'S MISTAKE

Sally, the servant-maid of Mr. A——, was accustomed to walk in her sleep. She one night came into her master's room, went into his bed, laid down and slept between him and his wife.

In the morning Mr. A—— got up according to his usual custom, a little after five o'clock, after having performed (as he thought) the part of an affectionate husband, not suspecting that there was anybody in bed with him but his wife.

He had not got downstairs before Mrs. A—— awoke, and accosted Sally, whom she mistook for her husband, in the following

terms: 'My dear Mr. A——, indeed I am not surprised that we have
no children, since you are so lazy. Come closer, my dear, pray my
dear, come, I am sure I am young and vigorous and perform my part
as well as any woman in the kingdom'.

Here Mrs. A—— paused a few minutes, waiting for an answer,
but receiving none from the imagined husband (who lay all the time
in a cold sweat, fearing a discovery, for she thought Mrs. A——
was her gallant the shopman, who laid with her every night, as she
was afraid to sleep by herself; but they never spoke to each other
during their amorous interviews for fear of being overheard.)

'Fellow, do you think me worthy of an answer; I'll be revenged
—I'll never get into bed with you again!'

Here her breast swelled so with anger that she could not utter
another word.

Fortunately it was not yet light, so Sally jumped out of the bed
and ran up to her gallant, to whom she imparted the whole affair.

This was the first time they had ever broken silence during their
amours, and they were overheard by another maid who slept in the
next room. She watched for the shopman's coming out of Sally's
chamber, and made him go into hers to gratify those desires which
I leave the reader to guess.

They all arose at their usual time, and Mrs. A—— being informed
that breakfast was ready, went downstairs into the parlour, and had
just seated herself when Mr. A—— entered the room, and accosted
her in the following words:

Mr. A—'Well, my dear, what do you think of me now?'

Mrs. A.—'That you are as incapable as a eunuch'.

Mr. A.—'Nay, my dear, I thought you seemed so much pleased
with our gambols this morning that we should have been very
great friends all the day, but, alas, I find there is no satisfying a
woman!'

Mrs. A.—'I'll tell you, fellow, I'll have a divorce. Not even
answer me, scoundrel. Did I not make a man of you? Had it not
been for me, you would have had to carry your cod-piece to a
beggar woman ere this—whilst I know by your unnatural abstinence
you have a gay woman in keeping—some painted little bitch or
flaghopper. Not a civil answer, when I offer you my love? You shall
repent it, sir, you old whoremonger, thus to neglect your virtuous
wife' (clapping her hands in fury).

Mr. A.—'My dear, I did. As I love my money, will you have it cut

53

off and preserved like a snake in a bottle—or do you want it twice before breakfast?'

Mrs. A.—'Your money is my money, and so ought your—— to be, but you take it elsewhere, you old adulterer!'

Mr. A.—'Nay, nay, my dear, but I believe you're too loving, my jewel, as soon as breakfast is over I'll lock the door and we will——'.

Mrs. A.—'Now, indeed, my dear, you speak like a man of mettle, and I forgive all that is past'.

When breakfast was over he performed his promise. Madam was pleased, and harmony once more reigned in their loving abode. Sally also was equally happy in having escaped from her dangerous predicament, her fellow servant in having gotten a gallant, and the shopman two fine girls to play and toy with at his pleasure.

Moral.—'It's an ill wind that blows nobody any good'.

THE ARITHMETICIAN—A FACT

Come tell me, dear Charlotte, my goddess, I cried;
    What numbers have tasted thy charms?
Too fickle enslaver! thou ownest a pride,
    In admitting a host to thine arms!
Yet blooming in all the luxuriance of youth
    The hills of thy bosom belie thee,
Then come my enchantress, confess me the truth,
    Let not prudery idly deny me!

O never, she cried, let us reckon the 'number,'
    But rather the 'length' of our loves!
Ah! give me full measure! and if it be under,
    I reckon by couples my 'doves,'
With my finger I spann'd every member of pleasure,
    Together I spann'd the amount,
Till the pricks put together, were twelve miles in measure,
    And then I gave o'er the account!

Song and the Marriage Morn

SONG

If anxious Venus, beauty's queen!
    Your empire should endure,
Borrow Cecilia's face and mien,
    Our homage to ensure.

Though perfect all the charms may seem,
    That famed Apelles drew.
Not half so sweet are they, I deem,
    As fair Cecilia's Cu.

The feelings of my faithful heart,
    My mouth shall still express,
Upon that Cu—, delicious part,
    In rapture's wild caress.

Oh! ye, who ne'er disquiet felt,
    Nor aught but virtue knew.
Whence is it? But your eye ne'er dwelt
    Upon Cecilia's Cu.

Cecilia, think not, from my brain,
    The souvenir can remove,
Of thy sweet Cu, 'twill there remain,
    Imprinted fast by Love!

But if my thread of life should break,
    Expire thy lover true,
May I flight 'mid kisses take,
    Imprinted on thy Cu!

THE MARRIAGE MORN

Tune—The Merry Dance

The marriage morn I can't forget,
    My senses teem'd with *new delight;*
    Time, cry'd I, haste the coming night,
And Hymen, give me sweet Lisette:
    I whisper'd softly in her ear,
    And said, 'The God of Night draws near'.

55

Oh, how she look'd! Oh, how she smil'd! Oh, how she sigh'd!
She sigh'd—then spent a joyful tear.

Now nuptial Night her curtain drew,
    And Cupid's mandate was, 'Commence
    With ardour, break the virgin fence'.
Then to bed sweet Lisette flew,
    'Twas heav'n to view her when she lay,
    And hear her cry, 'Come to me, pray'.
Oh, how I feel! Oh, how I pant! Oh, I shall die—
    Shall die before the break of day!

Soon Manhood rose with furious gust,
    And Mars, when he lewd Venus view'd,
    N'er felt his pow'r so closely screw'd
Up to the standing post of Lust;
    But when the stranger to her sight,
    Sweet Lisette saw in rampant plight,
Oh, how she scream'd! Oh, how she scream'd! Oh, how she
    scream'd!
    She scream'd—then grasp'd the dear delight!

Now lustful Nature eager grew,
    And longer could not wanton toy;
    So rushing up the path of joy,
Quick from the fount Love's liquor flew;
    At morn, she cry'd, 'Full three times three,
    The vivid stream I've felt from thee;
Oh, how I'm eas'd! Oh, how I'm pleas'd! Oh, how I'm
    charm'd!
    I'm charm'd with rapt'rous three times three!'

LA ROSE D'AMOUR;

Or the Adventures of a Gentleman in search of Pleasure.
Translated from the French.

(From Chapter VII)

I felt considerably enervated for a day or two and refrained from again entering the lists of Venus until I had fairly set sail on my projected cruise in search of love and beauty in the Hesperian climes, where I hoped for the most exquisite pleasure in the arms of the ardent ladies of Cuba and Spanish Main.

I coasted round and put into Bordeaux for the purpose of giving the sailors a chance of getting themselves girls.

In two days they were all mated, and we put off for Havana, intending to stop there a short time, as I had heard much of the beauty of the women of the island.

Arriving at Havana, I took some rooms at one of the best hotels, giving orders to the Captain to keep the brig in sailing order so as to be able to sail at a moment's notice.

At the *table d'hôte* I noticed a handsome, vivacious brunette, evidently an inhabitant of the island. Her eyes were fairly hidden under a mass of deep black hair which over-shadowed them; but I could perceive whilst at the table, she was continually glancing at me, and the moment my eyes met hers she would suddenly drop her eyes on the plate or look in another direction. From this I augured favourably and deemed success certain, thinking that I had made a conquest.

In the evening I attended the theatre accompanied by the Captain, and both of us well armed. I there saw the lady in a box in company with a couple of elderly gentlemen. The one whom I took to be her husband was a cross-grained, ugly looking fellow.

I followed her home with the intent to win her.

In the morning I got an introduction to Señor Don Manuel Vasquer, the husband of Donna Isabel, my lovely vis-à-vis at the table.

I told him I was a gentleman of rank and fortune, travelling for the pleasure with a vessel of my own, and invited him down to the harbour to look at the brig.

He accepted the invitation and was very much pleased with the

57

neat cleanliness of everything on deck, and with the luxury displayed
in the fittings of the cabin.

I had a lunch set out and plied him well with champagne so that
when he left the vessel, he was in very high spirits. On reaching the
hotel he invited me up to his apartment and introduced me to his
wife and a couple of other ladies we found with her.

I endeavoured as well as my looks could express to let her see
that I had taken particular notice of her, and was much smitten by
her charms.

After conversing for a short time I retired to my room to dress
for dinner and penned a declaration to the Donna Isabel, declaring
my passion for her and imploring her to grant me an interview, as
I had read in her eyes that I was not disagreeable to her.

After dinner I joined her and her husband and slipped my note
into her hand, which she immediately hid in the folds of her dress.
I then went to my room to wait for an answer, which I felt sure
would soon be sent to me. Nor had I to wait long, for in a couple
of hours a negro-wench opened the door, poking her head in to
ascertain if I was in the room, threw a note to me, and shutting the
door without saying a word, retired.

I hastily picked up the note and opening it found my expectations
confirmed!

She granted me an interview. Her note stated that her husband
would go out to his plantations the next day and that at three o'clock
in the afternoon she would be alone taking her siesta.

The evening, night and morning hung heavily on me, and after
dining, I retired to my room, laid my watch on the table and sat
gazing at the dial to see the weary hours pass away; but as the
minute-hand pointed to three; the same black wench again opened
the door, poked her head in, looked round and drew back, leaving
the door open.

I jumped up and followed her to the rooms of her mistress.

Here I found Donna Isabel reclining in an elegant dishabille, on a
sofa. She held out her hand to me in welcome, which I took and
pressed to my lips.

She invited me to be seated and I placed myself on a foot-stool
at her side. Taking her hand between mine, I disclosed my passion
for her, imploring her not to refuse my love. At first she pretended to be much surprised that I should make a declaration of my
love to her and appeared half angry. But as I proceeded with my

tale of love and pressed her for an answer favourable to the passion which was consuming me, she appeared to relent, and rising from her reclining position made room for me to sit beside her on the couch.

As I sat down by her side I dropped an arm round her waist and drawing her to my bosom I implored her to grant me her love— even to leave her husband and fly with me to some remote corner of the earth where we could while away our years in the soft dalliance of love.

I told her that her husband was an old man with whom she could not enjoy life, and from whom a young woman like herself could not receive those tender attentions, and the soft and real pleasure which she could enjoy in the arms of a young and devoted lover.

She sighed and hung her head on her breast, saying she never knew what it was to receive those delicious and tender pleasures from her husband that I had just spoken of. That from the time of her marriage to the present moment, his whole time was taken up with drinking and gambling. That he left her to amuse herself as best she could in the house, for he was so jealous that he would never allow her to go out except in his company. She sighed again and wished that heaven had given her such a man as myself.

I know not how it was, but when she stopped, I found one of my hands had opened the front of her dress and slipped beneath her shift and was moulding one of her large hard breasts, and my lips were pressed on hers.

My leaning against her had insensibly moved her backwards till, without our knowing it, her head was resting on the cushion of the sofa and I was lying on top of her.

Whilst I was assuring her of eternal love and constancy and begging her to allow me to give her a convincing proof of my tenderness and affection, and also to let me convince her that as yet she had had the mere shadow of the ecstatic pleasure of love, but that if she would allow me I would give her the real substance and a surfeit of those pleasures of which I felt convinced she had received but a taste from her husband, I had been gradually drawing up her clothes, till my hand rested on a large, firm, fleshy thigh. Isabel had closed her eyes, her head hanging to one side, her lips slightly apart and her breast rising and falling rapidly from the quick pulsations of the blood caused by her fierce and amorous desires.

I raised her shift still higher till it disclosed to my sight a large tuft of long black hair. I then unbuttoned my pantaloons and with a little gentle force parted her legs, and got between her thighs.

Parting the lips with my fingers, I inserted the head of my engine of love, and in a few moments we both died away amidst the most exquisite transports of love.

I lay heaving and panting on her bosom while she lay motionless under me, till finding that my stiffness had scarcely diminished and knowing by the short motions and jerks of the head that he was once more ready for the field and impatient for the word to start again, I commenced moving in her.

'Beautiful creature,' I cried, 'what delicious sensations! What pleasure! My God!' said I, 'you are almost virgin. How lusciously tight your sweet flesh clasps my rod!'

Her arms were clasped around my neck, her thighs around my back, her moist rosy lips glued to mine. Our tongues met. With what vivacity, what voluptuousness she moves up to me, giving me energetic heaves for my thrusts. I felt from the increased motion of her bottom that again she is about to dissolve herself into bliss. I too feel it.

'Ah, my God! Oh! what pleasure! I come, there, there, dear love, you have it now—joy, love, bliss unbearable!' And I was swimming in a sea of pleasure, in a perfect agony of bliss.

When we recovered from our delirium, I arose and drawing her clothes down slowly over her legs, I pressed her to my side. Planting a soft kiss on her pouting lips I folded her in my arms and asked her how she liked the reality after being fed for more than a year on the mere shadow of that delicious substance she had just largely partaken.

The answer was a kiss that sent a thrill of pleasure through every vein.

'Oh, my dear, this is nothing to what you would enjoy were you to link your fortune to mine and fly with me to France. Then we would have a life of love and pleasure such as you have just tasted. Our whole lives would be nothing but love and pleasure, morn, noon and night it would be love, all love. There should be nothing around us but love—nothing but pleasure!'

Isabel rang a small bell and the same piece of ebony who had twice placed her head in and out of my chamber-door entered.

Her mistress told her to bring in some lunch and she soon returned with an elegant cold repast and some delicious wine.

After eating and drinking we again turned our attention to love. Rising from the chair I led her to the sofa, and drawing her on my knees, I stripped her dress and shift from her shoulder and loosening the strings of her petticoats toyed and played with her breasts, which were really beautiful, large and firm, and tipped with two most tempting strawberry nipples.

Nor was my companion idle, for whilst I was thus engaged she had unbuttoned my pantaloons. I raised her on her feet and all her clothing slipping on to the floor, she stood in all her naked beauty before me.

What charms, what beauties did my eyes and lips feast on as I turned her round and round. Her soft round belly, her plump bottom and then her dear little cleft, that masterpiece of beauty, how I hugged it to me. What kisses I lavished on it, all of which she repaid with interest.

She sinks down on the floor between my legs ... a few motions and I most plentifully bedewed her with the nectar as she was paying down her own tribute to the God of Love.

In the evening she sent her black to order her supper to be sent up into her rooms, and after quietly supping we retired to bed and I spent the most agreeable night that I ever passed with any woman.

Her husband returned the next day, but I found an opportunity to meet his wife in the evening and renewed for a short time the transport we had enjoyed the day before.

A few days later, her husband had invited a party of six young ladies and the same number of young men to visit his wife and take dinner with them. I also was invited.

Immediately after receiving the invitation I sent word to the Captain to raise steam and be ready to sail at a moment's warning.

I joined the party at dinner and found three of the invited girls to be very handsome and the other three very goodlooking.

After the dinner was over, I invited the party to visit my yacht and take an evening's excursion with me.

The husband of my mistress was very loud in his praises of the beauty of the yacht and of the rich and elegant manner in which she was fitted up and joined his solicitations to mine; the party consenting, we ordered carriages and drove down to where the yacht lay. Getting aboard we sailed up the harbour and ran up the island.

After we were out of sight of the city, I took the Captain aside and told him that towards night I wanted him to run the brig in towards the shore; and that I intended to seize the seven men and land them in a boat and make off with the women. I told him to go and speak to the crew about the matter and have them in readiness to obey my signal.

A little before dusk, we ran close in shore at a place where there was no plantation visible. I had ordered some lumber to be strewn about the greater deck and commanded the Captain to send the sailors to carry it away.

Sixteen stalwart fellows came after and suddenly seized on the men and bound their arms and legs. I then told them what I intended to do, ordering the men at the same time to take the women below. Their execrations and implorings for the girls who were their relatives, I would not listen to, but I had them put in a boat and sent ashore. They were unbound and let loose. The boat returned to the brig and we set sail for France.

The girls did nothing but sob and weep for a day or two but I soon brought them to their senses. Immediately after setting their companions ashore I went into the cabin, and bringing Ibzaidu and Mary out of their hiding places, I introduced them to the company.

When supper was served they all refused to sit at the table and eat. But I told them if they did not comply with all my wishes that I would hand them over to the sailors to be used by them as they chose. This had its effect on them and they seated themselves at the table.

I rang a bell and two of the handsomest women belonging to the sailors entered stark naked, as I had ordered them to wait on the table.

The Spanish girls were all about to rise up, but putting on a fierce aspect, I threatened them the first who should rise would be passed forward to the men. This had effect on them and they sat still.

Whilst the servant was pouring out the coffee I arose and went to the side-table as if to fetch something, but in reality to pour a few drops of a certain liquid into each cup of coffee.

The quantity put in each cup was enough to set any woman's amorous and licentious desires on fire.

They all drank their coffee and in about half-an-hour the effect was very visible, as all the coyness of modesty had disappeared and they languishingly cast their lascivious glances at me, joking the servant-girls on their nudity, and whenever they came in reach of them, pinching, slapping them, etc., so great was the effect produced by the drug I put in the coffee.

When the supper was over and the tables were cleared, I commenced playing and tussling with them. Rolling them about on the floor and playing them a thousand amorous tricks which they repaid with interest—throwing me on the floor, falling in a heap on top of me while I would catch a kiss from them, squeeze a fine bubby, slide my hand along a thigh, or slip it up under their petticoats and grasp a large calf or a well-turned knee. I ordered in some wine of a very strong quality, well drugged with the love-potion.

I plied them with the wine of which they drank very freely and in a couple of hours all reserve and modesty had left them.

I took the Señora—the wife I had seduced at the hotel and whose husband I had set ashore with the others—on one side and invited her to step into one of the staterooms with me, I then asked her if she could forgive me for robbing her from her old cuckold of a husband. She threw herself into my arms and with a fervent embrace and kiss sealed my pardon with her lips.

THE BURIAL OF SIR JOHN THOMAS

Not a sound was heard, but the ottoman shook,
    And my darling looked awfully worried,
As round her fair form I a firm hold took,
    And John Thomas I silently buried.

We buried him deeply at dead of night,
    The tails of our night-shirts upturning;
With struggling raptures and fits of delight,
    The night-lights dimly burning.

No useless French Letters enclosed his crest,
    For ne'er in such rubbish we bound him;
But he went like a warrior taking his rest,
    With naught but his fur coat around him.

Few and short were the sighs we gave,
    Though we oftentimes groaned as in sorrow,
As each stroke for the joy we'd rave,
    Ne'er giving a thought for the morrow.

But as yet he had not nearly done,
    And ne'er had a thought of retiring,
When suddenly to groan we again had begun
    Through John Thomas silently firing.

And we thought, as he came from his narrow bed,
    As lifeless and limp as a willow,
How lowly he hung down his diminished head,
    And how gladly he'd rest on his pillow.

ENTERS LADY:

Lady—Is the Editor in?

Editor—Yes, Madame, what can I do for you?

Lady—I desire an article inserted and should like you to put it in for me.

Editor—Certainly, with pleasure, if you will first show it to me, so that I may see what it is like.

Lady—I wish a situation as a wet nurse and should like to get a good healthy boy.

(*Editor prepares this advertisement and shows it to the Lady, who likes the look of it and wishes it to be put in at once, and asks the price*).

Editor—How often shall you want it put in?

Lady—Well, I cannot tell! That will depend whether it is taken or not; but what will you charge for inserting it three times?

Editor—One dollar for putting it in three times.

Lady—Oh, how dear! You might do it for me for less!

Editor—No, Madame, we have so many ladies to oblige, that is our lowest price for inserting three times such an article as you ask for.

Lady—Well, suppose you do not get me a baby in three times, how much will you charge me for three times more?

Editor—Why Madame, if you can manage to keep the affair standing after that, for one dollar more I will put it in as often as you like, till I get you a child; that is, of course, provided the ink continues to flow.

THE NOVICE

A pretty little novice in her convent woke at dawn,
And looking for her lattice she spied upon the lawn,
    A handsome shepherd quite intent
On playing with his instrument, his instrument so long!

She raised the window softly and watched him for a while,
Delighted with his movements, then asked him with a smile:
    'Oh shepherd, pray, my wish consent,
And say what is that instrument, that instrument so long?

You play with it so nicely, it gives me joy to see,
So dear, I implore you, to teach the same to me;
    Oh, kind young shepherd, pray consent,
I'll finger well your instrument, your instrument so long!'

He looked up to her lattice with pleasure in his eye,
And cried: 'Come down, fair maiden, for there you are too high,
    Far, far too high for the extent,
That I can stretch my instrument, my instrument so long'.

She tarried not a moment, but swiftly rushed below,
And with the handsome shepherd she learned her lesson so
    That soon she played most excellent
Fantasies on his instrument, his instrument so long!

The first sweet lesson over for her too fast, she then
In winning tones addressed him: 'I'd like to play again'.
    Once more her fingers to work went,
Which made him use his instrument, his instrument so long!

E

Wicked Victorians

But strangers seemed approached, the fair girl bid him fly,
And cried: 'Oh, don't forget me, whene'er you travel by,
Oft, oft, come back, and we'll invent
Fresh tunes for that dear instrument, that instrument so long!'

66

A Night in a Moorish Harem

THIS novel, which appeared under the imprint of the Erotica Biblion Society, falls just outside the nineteenth century, its probable date being 1904. In both the spirit and the telling it is wholly Victorian, and its style and form has much in common with *Maidenhead Stories* which appeared some seven years before. A relatively short book of 145 pages, it contains fourteen brief narratives related by the author—the self-styled Lord George Herbert—and by the voluptuous inhabitants of the harem which he manages to invade accidentally after swimming from his ship. The style of the book is acceptably literate.

THE CAPTAIN'S SECOND STORY

'When I arrived at the age of fifteen I was still a slender stripling, but having had an intrigue with a lady's maid, I fancied myself quite a man of the world.

'One evening I attended the theatre with several other young noblemen. The play was *Antony and Cleopatra*. The character of Cleopatra was splendidly portrayed by an actress of Irish birth whom I will call Charlotte. She was of colossal size but of perfect proportions. The dark complexion of her lovely face made her a good likeness of the Egyptian queen whose voluptuous person and amorous nature she delineated so finely that every man in the house was carried away. Yet this magnificent woman was nearly fifty years old; her powerful constitution had triumphed over time.

'After the play was over we went into the green room and I was introduced to her; the charm of her person and form lost nothing on a nearer approach, though I detected one or two silver threads among her glossy hair. Her eyes had the brilliant sparkle of youth, her lips were plump and red and her teeth were as white as pearls. As soon as she heard my name she manifested a deep interest; a tender light came into her eyes and the colour heightened in her cheeks as she began to talk of my father. Now, I had heard of the trouble my father gave his friends in his youth by his infatuation with an actress. I could no longer doubt that she stood before me. Charlotte's name was free from scandal, remarkably so for an actress; perhaps her liaison with my father had been her only folly. "Do give a little supper party to meet me in my room after the play," she said to me. I promised to do so, and accordingly met there a few actors and patrons of the theatre.

'We had a modest supper, where wit and not wine reigned. I sat next to Charlotte, who seemed hardly able to take her eyes off me. When the guests began to go I lingered at the door and they went without noticing that I remained. The impulse was mutual to clasp each other in our arms. "Oh, how I wish that you had been my son; it should have been so!" she exclaimed. I was in no mood to be made a baby of. The grand, voluptuous form of the queenly actress aroused far different emotions when it was pressed to mine. "Is this your room?" I asked, drawing her towards the door. "For shame, George," she said, as crimson blushes spread from her cheeks to her splendid bosoms. She was in the costume of Cleopatra, over which she had thrown a long mantle after the play; this mantle had fallen off. It was evident that she had intended no assignation, for she moved reluctantly to the door, but she returned the passionate kiss I planted full on her mouth. So commanding was her height that she had to stoop slightly to do it. As soon as we entered the bedroom she sat down on the bed and covered her face with her hands. I took the opportunity to divest myself of most of my clothes. Then I stole up to her and kissed her naked and massive shoulder. She rose to her feet, and taking me in her arms as if I were a baby, she walked back and forth across the room with me.

' "Oh, Georgie, Georgie!" she cried, "this is almost incest, but I can deny you nothing; I who have allowed no man to embrace me since those delicious days of long ago!" She still carried me in her arms, walking to and fro. My face was in contact with her great bosoms, each of which was as large as my head. As I passionately kissed them my right hand dropped to her thighs, where it parted the loose oriental drapery. I lifted my face from her bosom and we exchanged a kiss. It differed from those she had heretofore given me; it was as voluptuous as my own, and was prolonged until I felt her other lips, which my hand was feeling, begin to swell and grow hot. Charlotte carried me rapidly to the bed. Her mood was changed from maternal tenderness to fiery passion. She lay me upon my back and sprang upon me. She folded me in her great, muscular arms and her ponderous thighs settled on my own; immense as they were, they felt as light as a young girl's. So firmly was I pinned to the bed by her great weight that I could not move; I felt as if I were about to be ravished like a woman. It was a new sensation, and as charming as it was novel. Charlotte suddenly turned over on her back without relaxing her hold upon me in the least. I found myself on top of her, but she was still mistress of the situation; her arms and legs were wrapped so tightly around me that my bones fairly cracked. It was the rapid undulation of her loins alone that moved our closely joined forms. Her mouth was fastened on mine as if she were about to devour me; her big womb pressed against my crest. I felt the crisis approaching overwhelmingly in the powerful embrace in which I was held. The rapture lasted in me for some time, even after I became nerveless, and at length died imperceptibly away.

' "Now you must go, you naughty boy," said Charlotte, tenderly kissing me and then spanking my bare bottom. "In ten minutes my maid will come to undress me, and it would never do for her to know that I had entertained you in my room". I was scarcely able to rise from her arms after such a long and exhausting embrace. I was like a squeezed and sucked orange; my vigour was all gone. It was fortunate that my ship was to sail the next day. I was a midshipman under my first orders, and I had to go. If the intrigue had been pursued I have no doubt it would have ruined Charlotte's reputation and also my health'.

Randiana

andiana; or Excitable Tales;
being the Experiences of An Erotic Philosopher appeared as from
New York in 1844, although its terminology indicates it to be of
English origin. It was actually printed c. 1884.

Randiana, originally of 127 pp, comprises twenty-four short chapters in the erotic life of 'an English gentleman'. It is passably well
written, containing no extravagant orgies, and called forth from
Ashbee the remark that it was 'a veritable *bonne bouche* after the
many tedious talentless bawdy tales which have been noticed in the
foregoing pages'. The style and manner of the chapters range from
what today would legally be judged to be obscene to the merely
mild and jokey. Here we reproduce Chapters 5, 9 and 23.

A BACHELOR'S SUPPER PARTY

Having become a frequent visitor at 'The Priory', the name Monsignor's hospitable mansion was generally known by, I had numberless opportunities for fucking Lucy, Madeline, and two of the domestics, but somehow I never properly took to flagellation in its true sense.

There was a housemaid of Monsignor's, a pretty and intelligent girl called Martha, the sight of whose large, fleshy bum, with an outline which would have crushed Hogarth's line of beauty out of time, used to excite me beyond measure, but I was not an enthusiast, and when Monsignor recognized this, and found that as a birch performer I laid it on far too sparingly, his invitations were less pressing, and gradually my visits became few and far between.

De Vaux, on the other hand, had become a qualified practitioner, and would dilate for hours on the celestial pleasures to be derived from skillful bum-scoring. In fact so perfect a disciple of Monsignor's did he get to be that the pupil in some peculiar phases has outstripped the master, and his work now in the press, entitled *The Glory of the Birch, or Heaven on Earth*, may fairly claim, from an original point of view, to be catalogued with the more abstruse volumes penned by the Fathers, and collated and enlarged by Messrs. Peter, Price, and Boniface upon the same subject.

As I stated before, I could not enter so thoroughly into the felicity of birching. I saw that, physically speaking, it was productive of forced emission, but I preferred the easy transition from a kiss to a feel, and eventually to a more natural sequence of a gentle insertion of the jock. I, therefore, to quote the regretful valediction of De Vaux, relapsed into that condition of paphian barbarism in which he found me.

But I was by no means idle, my income, which was nearly £7,000 per annum, was utilized in one direction only, and as you shall hear, I employed it judiciously in the gratification of my taste.

In the next suite of chambers to mine lived a young barrister, Sydney Mitchell, a dare-devil dog, and one whose *penchant* for the fair sex was only equalled by his impecuniosity, for he was one of that many-headed legion who are known as briefless.

I had occasionally, when he had been pounced upon by a bailiff, which occurred on an average of about once a month, rescued him by a small advance, which he had gratefully repaid by keeping me company in my lonely rooms, drinking my claret and smoking my best Havanas.

But this was to me sufficient repayment, for Sydney had an inexhaustible store of comic anecdotes, and his smartly told stories were always so happily related that they never offended the ear, while they did not fail to tickle the erective organs.

One morning Sydney came to me in a devil of a stew.

'My very dear Clinton', he said, 'I'm in a hell of a scrape again; can you help me out of it?'

'Is it much?' I said, remembering that I had paid £25 for him a few days before.

'Listen, and you may judge for yourself. I was at my Buffalo lodge last night, got drunk, and invited about half-a-dozen fellows to my chambers this evening to dinner'.

'Well,' I remarked, 'there's nothing very dreadful about that'.

'Yes, there is, for I have to appear as a substitute for a chum in the Queen's Bench in an hour, and my wig is at the dresser's who won't part with it until I've paid up what I owe, which will swallow up every penny I had intended for the dinner'.

'Oh, that's easily got over,' I said, 'ask them to dine here instead, say you quite forgot you were engaged to me, and that I won't let you off, but desire they accompany you'.

'I'm your eternal debtor once more,' cried Sydney, and he rushed off to plead as happy as a butterfly.

I ordered a slap-up dinner for eight from the neighbouring restaurant, and as my 'Inn dinners' were well known by repute, not one of the *invités* was missing.

We had a capital dinner, and as Sydney's companions were a jolly set, I made up my mind for a glorious evening. Little did I know then how much more glorious it was to wind up than ever I had anticipated.

When the cigars and the O.P. came on, and the meeting was beginning to assume a rather uproarious character, Sydney proposed that his friend Wheeler should oblige with a song, and after that gentleman had inquired whether my fastidiousness would be shocked at anything *ultra* drawing-room, and had been assured that nothing would give me greater pleasure he began in a rich clear voice the following:

Wicked Victorians

As Mary, dear Mary, one day was a-lying
As Mary, sweet Mary, one day was a-lying,
She spotted her John, at the door he was spying,
With his tol de riddle, tol de riddle, lol de rol lay.

His tol de riddle, tol de riddle, lol de rol lay.
Oh Johnny, dear Johnny, now do not come to me,
Oh Johnny, pray Johnny, oh do not come to me,
With your tol de riddle, tol de riddle, lol de rol lay.
Chorus—With your tol de riddle etc.

But Johnny, dear Johnny, not liking to look shady,
But Johnny, sweet Johnny, not liking to seem shady,
Why he downed with his breeches and treated his lady
To his tol de riddle, tol de riddle, lol de rol lay.
Chorus—To his tol de riddle, etc.

Oh, Johnny, dear Johnny, you'll make me cry murder,
Oh Johnny, pray cease this, you'll make me scream murder.
But she soon changed her note, and she murmured 'in further'
With your tol de riddle, tol de riddle, lol de rol lay.
Chorus—With your tol de riddle, etc.

Now Mary, dear Mary, grew fatter and fatter,
Now Mary's, sweet Mary's plump belly gew fatter,
Which plainly did prove that her John had been at her,
With his tol de riddle, tol de riddle, lol de rol lay.
Chorus—With his tol de riddle, etc.

MORAL

Now all you young ladies take warning had better,
Now amorous damsels take warning you'd better,
When you treat a John make him wear a French letter,
On his tol de riddle, tol de riddle, lol de rol lay.
Chorus—On his tol de riddle, etc.

74

A Bachelor's Supper Party

The singing of this song, which I was assured was quite original, was greeted with loud plaudits, then one of the young gentlemen volunteered a recitation, which ran as follows:

On the banks of a silvery river,
    A youth and a maiden reclined;
The youth could be scarce twenty summers,
    The maiden some two years behind.
Full up and a neck well developed,
    That youth's ardent nature bespoke,
And he gazed on that virtuous maiden
    With a look she could hardly mistake.
But the innocent glance of that virgin,
    Betokened that no guile she knew,
Though he begged in bold tones of entreaty,
    She still wouldn't take up the cue.
He kissed her and prayed and beseeched her,
    No answer received in reply,
Till his fingers were placed on her bosom,
    And he crossed his leg over her thigh.
Then she said, 'I can never, no never,
    'Consent to such deeds until wed;
'You may try though the digital process,'
    That maiden so virtuous said.
And he drew her still closer and closer,
    His hand quick placed under her clothes,
And her clitoris youthful he tickled,
    Till that maid excited arose.
'Fuck me now, dear, oh, fuck me,' she shouted,
    'Fuck me now, fuck me now, or I die'.
'I can't, I have spent in my breeches,'
    Was that youth's disappointing reply.

Monsignor Peter had, after an infinite amount of persuasion, given me the address where Pinero Balsam was to be obtained, and I had laid in a decent stock of it, for though each small bottle cost a sovereign, I felt morally sure that it was the nearest approximation to the mythical *elixir vitae* of the ancients that we moderners had invented. Some of this I had secretly dropped into the port of wine, and the effect upon my guests had already become very pronounced.

75

'I say, Clinton,' said the Junior of the party, who had only 'passed' a month before, and who might be just turned twenty, 'your dinner was splendid, your tipple has a bouquet such as my inexperience has never suggested, have you anything in the shape of petticoats about half so good? If so give me a look in'.

The youth was rapidly getting maudlin and randy; just then came a faint rap at the door. It was the old woman who swept and garnished the 'diggings'.

'I thought I might find Mr Mitchell here, sir,' she said apologetically, 'here's a telegram come for him,' and curtsying, the old girl vanished, glad to escape the fumes of wine and weed which must have nearly choked her.

'No bad news, I hope,' I said.

'Not at all,' said Sydney. 'What's the time?'

'Nearly 8:30,' I replied, consulting my chronometer.

'Then I shall have to leave you fellows at nine; my married sister Fanny arrives at Euston from the north on the 9:30'.

'What a pity!' said the callow Junior, 'if it were a sweetheart now one might be overjoyed at your good fortune—but a sister!'

'Is it the handsome one?' put in Wheeler.

'Yes,' said Sydney, showing us the face in a locket, the only piece of jewellery, by the way, he boasted.

There was a silence as all clustered around the likeness.

'By Jove,' said Tom Mallow, the *roue* of the party, 'if I had a sister like that I should go clean staring mad to think she wasn't some other fellow's sister, so that I might have a fair and reasonable chance'.

I said nothing, but I fell in love with that face to such an extent that I felt there was nothing I would not do to possess the owner.

I, of course, presented a calm exterior, and under the guise of a host who knew his duty, plied them with rare old port, and proposed toast after toast and health after health until I had the satisfaction of seeing in less than three-quarters of an hour, every member of the crew so dead drunk that I felt I could afford to leave the chambers without any fear of a mishap; then rolling the recumbent Sydney over, for he was extended prone upon the hearth-rug, I subtracted the wire from his pocket and saw that his sister's name was Lady Fanny Twisser.

'Oh,' I said, a light breaking in upon me, 'this then is the girl Sydney's mother married to a rich Baronet, old enough to be her grandfather; this doubles my chances,' and locking the door I made my way into the street. It was 9:19, and I was a mile and a quarter from the station.

'Hansom!'

'Yes, sir,'

'A guinea if you can drive me to Euston Station in ten minutes'.

That man earned his guinea.

A DISAGREEABLE MISTAKE

Not always have I had the happiness of being fortunate in my amours. It is true that I have managed to escape the dread fate of those poor unfortunate devils whose tools are living witness to the powers of caustic and the lethal weapons of surgery, but I have on occasions been singularly unfortunate, and as the warning voice of my publisher tells me I have little more time or space at my disposal, I will devote the present chapter of this work to detailing a most unpleasant incident, which all people are more or less liable to who go in for promiscuous intercourse to any large extent.

My only sister, Sophy, came up to London with her husband shortly after my return from Folkestone, and although he was a perfect brute of a fellow, and a man I disliked very much, I made myself as agreeable as I could, and took a furnished house for them during their stay, near the Regent's Park.

Frank Vaughan, a young architect, and a rising man, was one I introduced them to, as my sister had brought a friend, Miss Polly White, with her, who lived near our old home in the country, and being anxious to see London, her parents had placed her under my sister's guardian wing to do the 'lions' of the metropolis.

Polly was an only daughter, so knowing the old people had a good nest egg, I thought it would be a capital opportunity to throw Frank in her way.

I told him precisely how matters stood, and advised him to make a match of it.

'The old people are rich,' I said, 'but if they object to you on the score of money, fuck her, my boy, and that will bring them to reason'.

77

'Is she perfectly pure now,' said Frank, 'for to tell you the truth I haven't come across a genuine maid since I landed a stripling of thirteen, nearly ten years ago. Are you sure you haven't?'

'I'll swear it, if you like,' I returned, laughing at the soft impeachment, 'but take my advice, Frank, and win her. She'll be worth at least 40,000 when the old folks snuff it'.

'I'm on the job,' said Frank; and it was easy to see from the immaculate shirt front, the brilliant conversation, and the great attention he paid her, that he meant business.

One night, however, I was puzzled, for I thought Frank was far more assiduous in his manner to my sister than he should have been, considering that the 'nugget', for so we had christened Polly, was present.

I could not understand it at all, and determined to watch the development of the situation.

There was, I must tell you, an underplot to all this, for several times I had noted that Polly's regard for me was a trifle too warm, and once or twice in the theatre, and in the brougham, coming home particularly, I had felt the soft pressure of her knees, and returned it with interest—but, to my story:

Frank proposed going to Madame Tussaud's, and as Polly had never been, and my sister knew every model in the show by heart, Frank suggested that he should take the 'nugget', 'unless you would like to go with us,' he said to me.

'Not I, indeed,' was my reply, 'besides, Sissy here will be alone, as her beautiful husband has been out all day, and will, I suppose, turn up beastly drunk about midnight. No, you go together and enjoy your little selves'. So off they went.

When Polly passed me in the hall, she gave me a peculiar look, which I utterly failed to comprehend, and asked me to fasten her glove. As I did so she passed a slip of paper into my hand and when she had gone I read on it these words:

'Be in the study about nine o'clock'.

What can the little minx mean, was my first thought. She surely wouldn't go about an intrigue in this barefaced fashion; she has been brought up in a demure way, yet what on earth can she mean. At any rate I will do her bidding.

Making an excuse to my sister about eight o'clock, for I was as curious as possible to know what it could all portend, and saying I was going out for a couple of hours, I slammed the hall door behind me, and then quietly crept upstairs to the study.

I found it in darkness, but knowing where the couch was situated, at the far end of the room, I made for it, and I must confess the solitude, the darkness, and a good dinner, all combined, made me forget curiosity, Polly, the warning note, and everything else, and in less than five minutes I was fast asleep.

I was awakened by a scented hand I knew was a woman's touching my face and a low voice whispered in my ear—

'You are here then; I never heard you come in'.

Damn it, I thought, it's an intrigue after all; but she's too tall for Polly. Oh, I see it all, she's our prim landlady (who retained one room in the house, and was, I knew, nuts upon my brother-in-law). Polly found out about it, and set me on the track, so without saying a word I laid her unresistingly on the couch, and in a few seconds was busy.

I could not help thinking that she displayed much vigour for one of her years, since I judged the lady to be at least forty-five, but her ardour only made me the more fervent, and at the end of a long series of skirmishes the real hot short work began.

It would be impossible to express my horror at this moment when my hand came in contact with a cross she was wearing around her neck, and I found that it was my own sister I was rogering.

I had, unluckily, got to that point where no man or woman could cease firing, but the worst part of the damned unfortunate affair was that I burst out with an ejaculation of dismay, and she, too, recognized my voice. The situation was terrible.

'Good God!' I said. 'Sophy, how on earth has this come about?'

Then, sobbingly, she told me that her husband has abstained from her for more than two years because he had contracted a chronic gonorrhoeic disorder, and that Vaughan had won her over to make this *rendezvous*, and had intended letting Polly be shown through Tussaud's by a friend he had arranged to meet there. 'But,' she added, 'How was it I found you here?' This I dared not tell her, as it was now evident that Polly was aware of the assignation, and to let my sister know—that would have been death.

Poor girl, she was sufficiently punished for her frailty, and Polly, who had caught a few words of the appointment, was sufficiently revenged.

Polly never forgave my friend Frank for what she always considered his base desertion.

As for Sophy, I got her a divorce from her husband shortly afterwards. I give her an allowance myself, and I believe in my heart, that as women go, she is a very good one. I know that she has never ceased to pray for what she calls her great sin, but which I term my damned misfortune.

Polly married a brewer down in Devonshire, and as I have had several opportunities of testing her quality, I can assure my readers that the brewer has no cause to complain of his draw in the matrimonial lottery.

THE HISTORY OF FLAGELLATION
CONDENSED

'Gentlemen,' said Monsignor, lighting an exquisitely aromatized cigarette, for all priests, through the constant use of the censer, like the perfume of spices, 'first of all permit me to hope that you have enjoyed your dinner, and now I presume, De Vaux, your friend will not be shocked if we initiate him into some of the mysteries with which we solace the few hours of relaxation our priestly employment permits us to enjoy. Eh, Boniface?'

The latter, who was coarser than his superior, laughed boisterously.

'I expect, Monsignor, that Mr. Clinton knows just as much about birching as we do ourselves'.

'I know absolutely nothing of it,' I said, 'and must even plead ignorance of the merest rudiments'.

'Well, sir,' said Monsignor, leaning back in his chair, 'the art of birching is one on which I pride myself that I can speak with greater authority than any man in Europe, and you may judge that I do not aver this from any self-conceit when I tell you that I have, during the last ten years, assisted by a handsome subsidy from the Holy Consistory at Rome, ransacked the known world for evidence in support of its history. In that escritoire,' he said, 'there are sixteen octavo volumes, the compilation of laborious research, in which I have been assisted by brethren of all the holy orders affiliated to

Mother Church, and I may mention in passing that worthy Dr. Prince here, and Father Boniface have both contributed largely from their wide store of experience in correcting and annotating many of the chapters which deal with recent discoveries, for, Mr. Clinton, flagellation as an art is not only daily gaining fresh pupils and adherents, but scarcely a month passes without some new feature being added to our already huge stock of information'.

I lighted a cigar and said I should like to hear something more about it.

'To begin with,' began Father Peter, 'we have indubitable proof from the Canaanitish Stones found in the Plain of Shinar, in 1748, and unearthed by Professor Bannister, that the Priests of Baal, more than three thousand years ago, not only practised flagellation in a crude form with hempen cords, but inculcated the practice on those who came to worship at the shrine of their God, and these are the unclean mysteries which are spoken of by Moses and Joshua, but which the Hebrew tongue had no word for, therefore it could not be translated'.

'You astonish me,' I said, 'but what proof have you of this?'

'Simply this, it was the age of hieroglyphics, and on the Shinar Stone was found, exquisitely carved, a figure of the God Baal gloating over a young girl whose virgin nakedness was being assailed by several stout priests with rough cords. I have a facsimile in vol. 7, page 343—hand it to Mr. Clinton, Boniface'.

Boniface did so, and sure enough there was the Canaanitish presentment of a young maiden with her lovely rounded arse turned up to the sky, and her hands tied to the enormous prick of the God Baal, being soundly flogged by two stout-looking men in loose but evidently priestly vestments.

'The fact that the Israelites and Men of Judah were constantly leaving their own worship, enticed away by the allurements of the Baalite priests, is another proof of the superior fascination which flagellation even in those days had over such unholy rites as sodomy'.

'Your deductions interest me as a matter of history,' I said, 'but nothing more'.

'Oh, I think I could interest you in another way presently,' said Dr. Price.

Monsignor continued: 'The races all, more or less, have indulged in a love of the art, and it is well known that so far as Aryan lore

81

F

will permit us to dive into the subject, both in Babylon and Nineveh, and even in later times in India also (which is surely something more than a mere coincidence), flagellation has not only thrived, but has been the fashionable recreation of all recorded time'.

'I really cannot see,' I interrupted, 'where you get your authorities from'.

'Well, so far as Nineveh goes, I simply ask you to take a walk through the Assyrian Hall of the British Museum, where in several places you will see the monarchs of that vast kingdom sitting on their thrones and watching intently some performance which seems to interest them greatly. In the foreground you will perceive a man with a whip of knotted thongs, as much like out cat-o'-nine-tails as anything, on the point of belabouring something, and—then the stone ends, or in other words, where the naked-arsed Assyrian damsel would be, is *nil*. Of course this has been chipped off by the authorities as being likely to demoralize young children, who would begin to practice on their own posteriors, and end by fucking themselves into an early grave'.

'Well,' I said, in unbounded surprise, 'your research is certainly too much for me'.

'I thought we should teach you something presently,' laughed Dr. Price.

'I have thousands of examples in those sixteen volumes, from the Aborigines of Australia and the Maoris of New Zealand to the Esquimaux in their icy homes, the latter of whom may be said to have acquired the art by instinct, the cold temperature of the frozen zone suggesting flagellation as a means of warmth, and indeed, in a lecture read by Mr. Wimwam to the Geographical Society, he proved that the frigidity of Greenland prevented the women from procreating unless flagellation, and vigorous flagellation, too, had been previously applied.

'The patristic Latin in which the books of the Holy Fathers are writeen,' went on Monsignor, 'contains numerous hints and examples, but although Clement of Alexandria quotes some startling theories, and both Lactantius and Tertullian back him to some extent, I cannot help thinking that so far as practical bum-tickling is concerned, we are a long way ahead of all the ancients'.

'But,' observed Dr. Price mildly, 'Ambrose and Jerome knew a thing or two'.

'They had studied,' replied the imperturbable Father Peter, 'but

82

were not cultured as we moderns are; for example, their birches grew in the hills of Illyria and Styria, and in that part of Austria we now call the Tyrol. Canada, with its glorious forests of Birch were unknown. Why, sir,' said Monsignor, turning to me, his eyes lit up with the lambent flame of enthusiasm, 'do you know the King Birch of Manitoba will execute more enchantment on a girl's backside in five minutes than these old contrivances of our forefathers could have managed in half an hour. My fingers tingle when I think of it. Show him a specimen of our latest consignment, Boniface,' and the latter worthy rushed off to do his master's bidding.

To tell the truth I scarcely appreciated all this, and felt a good deal more inclined to get upstairs to the drawing room, when just at this moment an incident occurred which gave me my opportunity.

The bonny brunette, Madeline, looked in at the door furtively and apologized, but reminded Monsignor that he was already late for vespers.

'My dear girl,' said the cleric, 'run over to the sacristy, and ask Brother Michael to officiate in my absence—the usual headache— and don't stay quite so long as you generally do, and if you should come back with your hair disheveled and your dress in disorder, make up a better tale than you did last time'.

The Merry Order
of St Bridget

curiosity rather than a voluptuarian's delight, this novel is unusual in that it bears the name of an 'author', Margaret Anson, but not so unusual in that it deals wholly with flagellation, a subject to which some clandestine and semi-clandestine literature today remains devoted. Save doubtless for those who are addicted to this 'perversion' in its milder form, as distinct from the nightmares of de Sade, *The Merry Order* is a total bore. In the manner typical of much 'spanking' literature, it contains virtually no sex. It was printed in America in 1868, but by 1873, when the publisher died, only fifty copies out of five hundred had been sold or otherwise distributed.

The story is told through the medium of twelve letters describing the repetitive pranks of the Merry Order, a whipping club founded by a group of ladies in a French chateau. Ashbee considered that the book might have had its origins in an account of a female whipping club, which was said to meet on Thursdays in Jermyn Street—a fantasy recounted in *The Bon Ton Magazine* for December 1792. An actual account of male flagellation in a Victorian brothel is related by Walter in *My Secret Life*: it is one of the tawdriest and saddest accounts therein.

Flagellation, like rubber fetishism, is primarily a matter of lonely fantasy-making. As mirrored in much of its literature, it is often an end in itself since there are flagellation novels (some contemporary examples today occur in typed and duplicated form), in which no sexual acts as such are described, though they are occasionally inferred. A similar phenomenon occurs in the clandestine literature of sexual fetishists: see *The Outer Fringe of Sex*, by Maurice North (Odyssey Press, London, 1970). In *The Merry Order*, however, flagellation is treated, albeit dully, with romantic and almost rococo overtones.

Letter VIII

THE WOMAN IN WHITE

My Dear Marion,

I promised to tell you about the installation of Mme. Hautville to a place in the Order of St. Bridget. It took place at the very next meeting after I had caught Gustave and he had been whipped. There was nothing new to be done—whipping is whipping, and nothing can make it different. But the ladies resolved to have something fresh about it, and agreed, that instead of all having the orthodox rods they should have as many kinds of instruments of punishment as they could think of; thus, one lady should use a slipper; another a birch, tightly tied; another a loosely-fastened rod, and so on. Mrs. D—— declared for nothing at all: she would use the palm of her hand only, she said, 'and if I don't make as much impression as any of you,' she added, wickedly, 'why, I have forgotten my practice, that's all'.

Mme. Hautville made a very pretty toilette for the occasion; she was all in white, not a penitent like the Princesse had been for her admission, but in the costume of a novice when she takes the veil. The dress had been considerably modified as being too flowing for the occasion, but it was all white silk and lace, and a lovely little angel she looked when it was completed. From head to foot she had nothing on that was not pure white. What satin shoes, with diamonds sparkling on the rosettes; white silk stockings, gartered above her round knees with white velvet garters, with satin rosettes; white petticoats—one of the finest flannel, embroidered with lilies, and one of soft lawn, with a lace flounce. Her robe was silk, the soft noiseless sort that does not rustle, richly trimmed with costly Mechlin lace, and over her head she had a square veil. She had Gustave in to assist at her toilette, and allowed him to put on her exquisite stockings, and fasten her garters and shoes. I could see the delight the mischievous rogue felt in doing it; his face flushed, and his hands trembled so that he could hardly clasp the silver fastenings. But Madame never minded him a bit; she seemed rather to like feeling his hands about her, and very nice hands they had grown into by now, I can assure you. He looked wistfully after her as we escorted her downstairs, but he dared not follow this time. Madame submitted to be blindfolded with a very good grace, though she tried hard to get me to tell her what was going to be done; she had such pretty coaxing ways that it was hard to resist her; but I did, and she went in quite unprepared. We led her slowly up the room, and at the first stroke of the rod, nearest the door, she winced, but did not cry out; the next blow she received was a stinging one from a slipper my lady held in her hand (she knows how to strike with a shoe, I can tell you), and she gave a little scream and a jump. 'Oh, what is it?' she said, between her teeth; but the next stroke, a fair open-handed slap from Mrs. D——'s fat hand, made her fairly shriek out, and twist herself out of our grasp on to the floor. It was a slap, and rang out even above the laughter of the ladies, leaving a broad red mark on the white, firm flesh of the little lady.

'Stop punishment!' said Lady C—— from her dais; 'the applicant will answer the questions of the Merry Order before she is further whipped'.

We led her to the ottoman, and she knelt over it.

'Angeline Marie Hautville,' she went on, 'you promise to obey the Merry Order of St. Bridget in all things pertaining to their rites?'

'I do'.

'And to answer all questioning from their president?'

'I do'.

'You are accustomed to the practice of the rod?'

'I am'.

'And have a passion for it?'

Mme. Hautville bowed, but made no answer.

'Your husband joins you in the practice?'

Another mute bow, and the fair face turned fiery red, no doubt at the thought of that same private practice, and how it must have been seen by some one.

'State to the Merry Order how you became acquainted with the use of the whip, and whether you or M. Hautville was the first to introduce its pleasures into your married life?'

Again she blushed, and did not immediately speak; and Lady C—— repeated her question, when she replied in a low tone, 'I was'.

'You first taught your husband to find pleasure in whipping?'

'I did'.

'And where did you learn it yourself?'

'In the convent where I was brought up'.

'Was it practised there as a punishment only, or as a pleasure as well?'

'Both—as a punishment by the sisters and priests, and as a pleasure by the girls of the covent school, who learned the use of the rod from their superiors'.

'You have not told your husband of our meetings and your intentions?'

'I have not'.

'And you will not?'

There was a difficulty in the answer to this question. Mme. Hautville would say no more than, 'Not if I can help it,' which caused much laughter and some consternation, though the ladies agreed amongst themselves, that as M. Hautville practised whipping himself he would not be likely to say anything even if his wife did let the secret out. Whether she did or not, he held his tongue; and I heard my lady remark that he was exceedingly attentive to and careful of her the next day, when she kept her room. The whipping she got was a pretty severe one; the different kinds of instruments used made the punishment harder to bear than the continuous stroke of a single rod, and her poor hips were all weals and bruises. When I took her away to her room Mlle. St. Kitts went with her, and remained in her rooms; she and that lively young lady took a fancy to one another at once, and Mademoiselle sympathized with her in her sufferings. Mlle. St. Kitts was an orphan, or she would never have been admitted. She was staying at the chateau under the protection of her aunt, Mlle. Loupe, one of the above-mentioned old maids, a cross, strait-laced creature, but quite powerless to control the wayward girl, who was to all intents and purposes her own mistress. She lectured her severely upon her joining 'those women' as she called the ladies, and vowed she would make the Count put an end to their secret meetings.

'The Count would be only too glad to join us, aunty,' she replied; and indeed, when Mlle. Loupe spoke to him indignantly about the proceedings of the tabagie, he replied, 'That so far from trying to stop the amusements of his guests, he intended to apply for admittance to their meetings himself, for he was sure that what ladies could keep secret with such pertinacity must be intensely interesting and amusing'.

Mlle. St. Kitts related all this at the next meeting of the society, to the amusement and indignation of the sisterhood, and added, that her aunt was excessively curious about their ceremonies.

'I think the best plan would be to enlighten her', said Mrs. D——, with a laugh, and she drew her rod through her fingers as she spoke. 'What, admit her!' said Lady C——. 'I don't think we should find her an agreeable associate, nor a silent one either'. 'I don't think we should; but we might initiate her for all that: let her have a taste of our proceedings and I don't think she would want any more, or would be likely to go tattling to the Count again. We'll leave Mlle. St. Kitts out of the scheme if she likes'.

'Oh no! I owe auntie a grudge for many a bit of spite, and if you don't serve her worse than you served me I shan't grumble, and she'll be none the worse'.

'Half the whipping will do, my dear, but I think we can cure her of curiosity, and complaining too,' replied Mrs. D——; and then, rising, she begged permission to lay before the meeting a plan of revenge upon Mlle. Loupe for her ill-will towards the society. It was received with much laughter and approbation; and it was resolved that if the lady showed any more animosity it should be immediately carried out. They had not to wait long. The very next day the fair lady again assailed the Count with a request that he would deprive the ladies of the use of the smoking room, and put down the 'disgusting orgies' held there. The Count repeated her words to my lady, and the sisters resolved upon instant revenge. When Mlle. Loupe retired that night to her room she found a note upon her dressing-table, inviting her to join the rest of the ladies in the tabagie the next evening. It further directed her to knock at the door of the smoking-room at a certain hour alone, otherwise she would not be admitted. The note concluded by saying the ladies trusted to be able to convince her of the complete harm-lessness of the secret society, about which she had so kindly inter-ested herself. She went to her niece's room in great excitement to know who sent the invitation, but Hilda was mute upon the subject. 'She had heard the ladies express a wish to have her aunt join them,' that was all she could say about it; and Mlle. Loupe passed the night and the next day in a state of extreme excitement. The ladies met that night in their ordinary evening costumes, for reasons which will presently appear, except the two footmen and the page, who were on duty beside Lady C——'s chair. The room was almost in darkness; the only lights were two candles on the stands at the top of the room, and as soon as the knock was heard at the door these were blown out, leaving us in total darkness. This had been arranged before-hand, and the Princess's maid removed from her post of outside door-keeper. Mrs. D—— disguised her voice, which she had a knack of doing, and asked who was there? Mlle. Loupe answered timidly, and was immediately drawn into the room, and the same voice told her she must be blindfolded. In the twinkling of an eye, and before she could resist her hands were pinioned, and a handkerchief tied over her eyes. While this was being done the candles were lit, and a dozen hands seized upon the unlucky victim. Struggles were vain-screams of no avail; indeed, they were lost in the peals of laughter which resounded on all sides. Mlle. Loupe was prepared, horsed, firmly held on the back of one of the footmen, and soundly whipped. To describe her appearance would be vain. Fancy a scraggy, sallow woman, with skin like parchment, and a coiffure composed mainly of false hair, which loosened itself in her struggles and kept tumbling off; and a shrill voice, which now and then raised itself above the general tumult in a sharp squeal, which was more temper than pain, for the ladies laughed too much to make their blows very hard. A very few minutes sufficed to give each of them an opportunity to use their rods, and then one by one they glided silently from the room. The pins which held up her dress were taken out, and the bandage over her eyes loosened, and she slid to the ground to find herself alone with two men and a page. They stooped over her with well-acted surprise, but she shrieked and hid her face.

'Men too!' she screamed. 'Oh! oh! go away; it only wanted that to complete their wickedness. Go away, I tell you! How dare you come here? Send my maid you wretches—Mlle. Loupe's maid—oh, oh! they've murdered me'.

She was wasting her lamentations on the empty air, and when she looked up again she was alone. There was an empty room, not a trace of any occupancy remaining, and she rolled over again on the couch bewailing her smarts and the way she had been tricked. She must have lain there some time, when, getting a little calmer, she sat up upon the couch and confronted a man gazing at her, no less a person than the Count's valet, a very fine gentleman indeed, who had been passing the tabagie, and, attracted by unusual sounds, had entered, and was surveying Mlle. Loupe's disarranged dress and disordered coiffure with mingled admiration and astonishment.

'Another man!' she shrieked. 'Are you one of them? Are you leagued with the wretched women who meet here and indulge in such abominable practices? I have been——' she stopped suddenly, and said 'insulted, outraged in this room, and I will have reparation'.

'There is no one here but Mademoiselle,' the man replied, puzzled; 'the ladies are in the drawing-room; there has been no meeting in the tabagie tonight'.

'No meeting! Do you dare to stand there and tell me that when I——? Ah! I see you are one of them; perhaps one of the vile men who was here just now, hired by those women to insult me'.

'I will send Mademoiselle's maid to her,' was all the reply he condescended to make to her, and walked off to the drawing-room, where, after a little delay, he was able to speak to his master, and tell him that Mlle. Loupe had gone mad in the smoking-room.

'Is it a secret, Count?' asked the Princess, who had dressed and was moving about the room, delicately lovely in a pale primrose-coloured dress. 'Your face looks interesting'.

'Does it? It was a serious piece of news Andrea brought me, I can assure you; he says Mlle. Loupe is in the tabagie raving mad. Have you anything to do with this sudden alteration of her intellects?'

'I have done nothing to produce such a catastrophe as that'.

'I strongly suspect your sisterhood, who hold the secret conclaves yonder, have been practising upon her amiable nature. Ladies, shall we go and see how far Andrea's dismal tale is true?'

Down in a body went the Ladies, with the Count at their head, to gather round Mlle. Loupe, and question and condole with the utmost innocence. She spoke out plainly now, declared she had been shamefully outraged, whipped, and degraded in the presence of his servants, at a secret meeting of the ladies in the chateau.

'But, my dear madam, there has been no meeting here tonight, the ladies have given us the pleasure of their society in the drawing-room, where we have missed you, I can assure you'.

'You have been tricked, and so have I!' she said in a fury. 'I tell you I was beaten by two men in livery, and a page stood by and looked on; and I heard the laughter of a room full of people at my sufferings. Count de Floris, if there is a law in the land, I will have it!'

'Certainly, my dear madam; if you can point out the offenders, I will aid you to the utmost in bringing them to justice'.

'Point them out! They are your guests, these women who think nothing too shameless to indulge in their vile meetings'.

'I think we had better retire, Count,' said Mrs. D——, with dignity. 'Mademoiselle's malady appears to be one for which a night's rest will be the best remedy'.

'Dear, dear, how sad!' said the Princess, slyly 'I had no idea of anything of that sort; better ring for her maid, poor creature, and have her taken upstairs at once'.

The Count was puzzled, and half inclined to think that this guest had been indulging too freely in champagne at dinner, but he spoke gently to her. 'Indeed, my dear madam, you are under some delusion; if you will allow me to conduct you to your room, the matter will be most carefully investigated'.

There was nothing for it but to comply, and the next morning every servant in the house was strictly examined. No one knew anything about it, of course; none of the men had been near the tabagie on the previous night, and the women had only to report that they had dressed their ladies for the evening as usual, with no information regarding any meeting. It's my belief that the Count knew or guessed at the truth, and rather enjoyed the discomfiture of Mlle. Loupe: who, poor soul, remained under the imputation of having taken more wine than was good for her on that particular day, and who never attempted any more to meddle with the other ladies, or to interfere with the doings of Mlle. St. Kitts. It gave her a lesson she did not forget, and she was obliged to take it to heart in secret and without fuss. She had no witnesses to bring forward, and of course there was only her own word as to the whipping. She could not very well produce ocular proof of the fact, and her assertion did not go for much. She was a much more amiable woman after the little ceremony, which gave her an insight into the doings in the tabagie, than she was before; and it was a long time before she again tried to learn any of the secrets of St. Bridget. When she did—but that is too long a tale to tell now; I'll let you have it in its proper place. My lady is calling, so I must go—Believe me, as ever,

Your sincere friend
M. Anson

P.S.—My letter is quite long enough, but I may not be able to write again for some time, and I see I have been scribbling on without ever answering your question about Gustave. My lady only wanted me to give me some orders about her dress for a hunting party that is to come off next week, where they are all to be in Moyenage costumes, and make fools of themselves, by pretending to hunt the poor tame boar that has been kept in a pen in the woods here ever since we came.

My lady is going in a crimson dress, with gold trimming; Mme. Hautville, in blue and silver and the little Princess in green and gold. Old Lady C—— (and what a spectacle that woman will be on horseback, to be sure!) has composed a costume out of two old black velvet and satin dresses, and trimmed them with white and silver like a coffin; she'll look like an undertaker's advertisement. But all this has nothing to do with that imp of a page. You ask whether he took all the punishment he got quietly, and whether he did not retaliate upon us for his whippings. Of course he did, and in a way we little expected, and could not resent. There was a ball at Tours, a very select and genteel one, and most of the ladies and gentlemen at the chateau—I mean in our circle—were invited. We had some work to get permission, but as it happened on an evening when we were not much wanted we did get it, though I must not tell you how we were harassed till the very last minute, and barely allowed time to dress and get off. I was fully prepared two or three days beforehand: as I told you, my foot and my lady's are the same size, and though she is taller and stouter than I am, a little alteration makes her dresses fit me. I was resolved not to be outdone in the matter of dress, and I selected a blue and white shot silk, which had only been twice worn, and Honiton trimmings. There were shoes to match the dress, which my lady did not much like—she always said it did not suit her complexion. It did mine beautifully, and I can tell you that there was quite a buzz of admiration when I walked into the ballroom with M. Pierre, M. Hautville's valet. For ornaments, I had a garnet and pearl set belonging to my lady, and a perfumed fan, which had just come with a lot of other things from Paris. Fifine had much more trouble with her dress; she was taller and bigger than her little mistress, and she was obliged to content herself with a lace dress as the only one she could alter successfully. I helped her with gloves and shoes; and with some Paris diamonds and deep crimson flowers she looked very pretty. Gustave helped with our toilettes, and was very demure and

93

quiet all the evening—so quiet, that we could not help fancying he meant mischief.

'I know he's up to something,' Fifine said, as we drove off.

'Oh, Mademoiselle, suppose he was to go to our ladies and tell about these!'

She put her hand up to her neck where her mistress's ornaments glittered, and looked frightened, for the Princess had a temper, and was easily offended.

'Oh, no fear!' I replied. 'Gustave is not a bad hearted boy: he may play us some prank, but he won't do anything deliberately spiteful'.

The ball was a most delightful one; we were universally pronounced the belles of the room, and had more attention paid us than any other people of the place. It was late when we got home, and we found that Stephens, good-natured for once, had attended to our duties for us, and we could go to bed at once. Not a sign of Gustave was to be seen; the men said he was in bed long ago, and we went off to our rooms, glad to be rid of him, and tired enough. We undressed and folded up our dresses, which were none the worse, and chatted freely about the ball and what we had seen and done there. All at once I heard a smothered laugh somewhere; I was sure of it, but though we looked well about we could see nothing. Our lights were soon out, and I got into bed. I had left the door open, and could hear Fifine get into hers; a moment more, and she sprang out with a terrified scream.

'What is the matter?' I asked, and then there came a peal of mischievous laughter, and Gustave rushed past me, and in a moment had locked the outer door communicating with the corridor, and taken out the key.

'You little wretch!' I exclaimed. 'What do you want? Where were you?'

'In my bed,' gasped Fifine 'I—I——'

She could not speak between rage and fright, and the boy, who was half dressed, only laughed the more.

'That's just where I was,' he said; 'and now, you two girls, look here: I've let you whip me and lead me a precious life, and I'm going to turn the tables. I'm going to whip both of you, and try my hand, or else go straight to the Princess the first thing in the morning and tell her about the fine dresses I helped to put on'.

The little brute was quite in earnest. Not only had he been lying in bed in wait for us, but he had two rods there, which I knew at a glance had come from the Princess's store; and do you know, my dear, many things made me fancy afterwards that she knew about it —both the dresses and the whipping too. Well, to make a long story short, and to save myself I consented that Gustave should whip me —and the little wretch made me go through all the proper cere- monies, and then gave me as good a flogging as ever my mistress did. Fifine resisted for a long time, but she, like me knew what he could do to spite us if he chose in other ways besides the ball affair (for we had talked quite unrestrainedly before him), and she submitted at last. How the little wretch chuckled when he got hold of her, and we recovered our breath after the scuffle.

'Now, Mademoiselle,' he said, mimicking the Princess's voice to a nicety, 'kneel down and kiss the rod!'

Fifine hesitated, but a smart cut across her unprotected legs brought her to reason.

'Let him have his way,' I said; 'it is no good thwarting him'. So she knelt and did as he bid her, and he lectured her the while with such a serious face that I could not but laugh, though I was smarting, I can tell you.

'Mlle. Fifine,' he said, 'you have been guilty of a grave offence in wearing your mistress's dresses and jewellery; you will now take punishment for the same at my hands. Rise, and lean over the ottoman! Mlle. Anson, hold her hands!'

We both laughed—we could not help it; but Fifine saw it was best to submit, and she took her flogging quietly—the imp of mis- chief asking her whether it was not much nicer to be whipped by a fine handsome young man (fancy a monkey of fourteen calling himself a man) than by an angry mistress. At length he stopped, and Fifine was as sore as I was; she jumped up and made for the door.

'Oh, I haven't done with either of you!' he said, wickedly; 'that was only for the dresses: now about the jewels'.

In vain we protested and begged; he declared if we did not do all he required of us he would go to our ladies first thing in the morning and describe exactly what we had worn. There was nothing for it but to obey, and, standing by the chair where he had whipped us, he ordered us to turn up our night-dresses and fasten them. When he had done this he made us march before him round and round the room, administering alternate cuts to one and the other. I looked at Fifine, and she at me; we had had about enough of it, and when he once more sat down we put our own smarting hips out of the question, and sprang upon him, one on each side. In a twinkling he was down, and his head tied up in a towel; then his hands fastened, then his legs, and then he was at our mercy.

'Now it is our turn,' Fifine said, while I hastily undid the fastening of his trousers, the only clothing he had on, except his shirt.

'Oh let me go!' he begged. 'I won't tell; indeed, indeed I won't!'

'I don't intend you shall,' I replied; 'but we shall whip you in case you forget and let a word slip;' and, rolling him over, we administered a full payment for what he had given us.

He was not a vindictive fellow, for he never told; and as far as my lady was concerned our secret was safe. From a good many little things that slipped out I always fancied that the Princess was not so ignorant either of the dressing or the whipping, but she kept her own council, and we heard no more about it. But I must not write more now, for my lady will be back directly. Let me know when you get this, and believe me,

Your affectionate friend,
M. Anson

Maidenhead Stories

HIS collection of stories
first appeared c. 1894, with an indicated edition in America three
years later. It uses the 'Decameron' device of a gathered number of
men—here, college graduates—recounting their most memorable
dalliances. As in *Randiana* and *A Night in a Moorish Harem*, the
fifteen stories are fashioned with some professional skill, indicating
that this was one of a number of such books commissioned rather
than 'turned in' on chance. A twist to the proceedings is given
at the outset when, in order to spice the story-telling, one of the
graduates hies over to the nearest brothel and returns with 'two of
the handsomest and most shameless women of the town'.

Despite the setting of 'the final supper of the Beta Theta Pi's',
the style tends to indicate an English writer rather than a home-
grown American. Compare *Burton's Story*, which follows, with *The
Captain's Second Story*, from *A Night in a Moorish Harem* (p. 68
et seq.).

97

BURTON'S STORY: 'THE FANCY DRESS BALL'

When I was a little one, 14 years old, my mother took me and my sister to spend the summer at Jane's Springs in the mountains of Virginia. My father was then in Congress, then in session; he wanted his family near him so that he might run down and spend Sundays with us. I was quite a girlish-looking boy and as innocent as an iceberg. I was then a regular mama's pet and though, thanks to a splendid constitution, I liked to run and jump, still I had no playmates but my sisters—who by contrast were quite tomboyish—for I did not go to school, being educated by a governess. I tell you all this to show you how green I was and why I was so trusted. I did not play with the other boys, who quite despised me and left me to the girls who loved me. I was hugging and kissing them all the time on the sly; for some reason or other they let me do it and I must say that after these osculatory exercises I used to feel very warm and uncomfortable all over, although the discomfort was not so disagreeable after all.

The old hotel was built with piazzas in front on which the rooms opened, and therein inmates used to spend most of their time during the heat of the day. The room next to mine was occupied by the young wife of an attaché of the French legation, a beautiful brunette with a little figure, well-developed bust and the smallest hands and feet I ever saw. She was simply superb and her dresses, which my feminine training enabled me to fully appreciate, were marvels of beauty, elegance and style. The nights when her husband had time to run down from Washington, I used to hear all sorts of strange noises from the room, which only a thin partition separated from mine. I used to hear the violent creaking of the bed, choked sighs, exclamations, suppressed laughter, and often the sound of people rolling over and over. As their room was at the end of the house, mine was the only one where they could be heard and I suppose they didn't think that a young girl-boy like me counted for anything. I used to wonder what it meant at first, but soon supposed he was playing with her as I played with the girls, and yet I must say that these sounds made me feel very uncomfortable, much more so than I did when I hugged and kissed the maidens.

As the summer grew on, Madam X and I grew to be great friends. She was fond of talking French, which she called 'la langue de Dieu', and one of my accomplishments was a considerable proficiency in that elegant speech. We would spend hours together sitting under the trees reading to each other French novels, many pages of which I did not understand; when I asked her for an explanation, she used to smile in the strangest way, look at me sideways out of the corner of her magnificent eyes, and say that she couldn't then, but perhaps sometime. And the more I would ask, the more mischievous she would look, till finally, if I became too importunate, she would pull me into her lap, tickle me under my arms and under the knees and smother me with kisses. Then, in the evenings, I used to go into her room and she would recite the poetry of De Musset and Gautier by the yard. But in the real dark nights, she used to sit out on the piazza, up in the corner where people could not see us, and she would hold my head on her bosom, put my arms about her neck and then, in the most fascinating manner, kiss me on the eyes, behind the ears and press her soft lips upon mine, folding them softly and seemingly to draw my very soul out of me. Of course these things did not come all at once; it was a gradual crescendo up to the climax—but I shall never forget those dark, mysterious nights when her pale face gleamed above mine in the dim light from the garden lamp, her deep eyes glowing above mine and her luxurious hair becoming loosened and falling about my face, thrilling me with its electric touch. She told me I should say nothing to my mother —but I needed no such instruction; instinctively I felt that this was not to be told to anybody. Finally my mother went up to Washington to stay with my father for some reason that I have forgotten. Madam X, whom I now called 'Tante Madelon', promised to see that we were well taken care of and the maid did not neglect her duty.

A few days after my mother's departure, there was to be a fancy dress masquerade ball and, of course, we youngsters were just as much interested as the old folks. My sisters chose their costumes themselves, but I naturally went to Tante Madelon for advice. We discussed all sorts of things: sailor boys, pages, marquises and all the common stuff; but none suited Madelon; she must have something particularly recherché for her Henri. Suddenly her face, which had grown quite perplexed, lighted up—we were at her room at the time—and she said gleefully: 'Mais je tiens l'affaire. I have it certainement. See, you're just the height of me. We will dress just alike, we are both dark and will have a grand time'.

'What! go as a girl?'

'Yes; you will be a beauty, cheri, come let's try one of my dresses now. Take off your coat and vest and your little pantaloons, mon ami,' and she opened the trunk and began selecting a suitable robe. I stood abashed, not daring to move. What, take off my clothes before a woman? I knew she would laugh at me and I should die of shame.

She rose from the trunks with the dresses on her arms.

'What, not ready? Why, what's the matter?'

I tried to stammer a reply, but only choked and blushed.

'Oh, see how the little thing is modest,' she laughed, but turned crimson herself. 'You are not afraid of your Tante Madelon, are you cheri? Let me help you and then you shall help me. But remember, mon petit, this is a secret'.

With trembling fingers she unbuttoned my coat and vest and helped me off with them, then my trousers and shirt, leaving me in my undershirt, drawers and shoes.

'I'm afraid you can't wear my shoes,' she laughed, placing her pretty little foot beside mine, 'so you can keep them on, but that long-sleeved undershirt must come off'.

I made no resistance but was deadly pale and trembling all over. Off came my undershirt and she replaced it with a spotless chemise of hers. Then, slipping her hands underneath, she unbuttoned my drawers. As she did so, her burning hand touched a certain portion of my anatomy and sent a thrill through me that made me nearly faint away; with a laugh she noticed my trouble but went on remorselessly; then, bringing a pair of drawers she made me put them on. While she was toying there, I felt every touch of her fingers like points of burning flame. Then came the corset, which had to be let out but very little, as I was a remarkably slender youth. Then she brought a couple of shell-shaped cups of straw, which she thrust into the top part of the corset.

'What are these for?' I asked.

'Don't you know, my dear little innocent? They are to imitate these,' and taking one of my hands, she thrust it into her dress where it rested on the loveliest bosom imaginable. What my feelings were I can't describe now, but I remember this made me grow bolder and I said 'But you don't need any, Tante Madelon; you have enough of them'.

'No, of course I don't,' she replied, still keeping my hand in its warm and luscious nest, 'I only use them when I wear very tight dresses in order to keep the corset from hurting me'. Then she kissed me and tickled me and I returned her teasing abuses. At last she drew my reluctant hand away and went on with the dressing. With the aid of a few pins, the gauze muslin dress, which was quite loose and flowing, was accommodated to my form.

'Now, look at yourself in the glass,' she said, 'how you would fascinate men if you were only a girl!'

I must say myself, now you must just stop that laughing, that I was quite a matter in white muslin.

'Now shall I not help you to dress, Tante Madelon?'

'What do I want to dress for,' said she, her eyes flashing and her face crimson—probably from the excitement of dressing me, though perhaps from some other reason. 'I know how I shall look; I shall look just like you. And with our masks on no one will be able to tell us apart. Won't we have fun? We will retire just before they unmask and then no one will ever know who we were.'

'But,' she said reflectively, 'I must go to Washington for some shoes, gloves and slippers for you—you never could get into mine, you dear little fascinator. Oh how sweet you are!' And she seized me with her arms, kissing me wildly, this time thrusting her rosy tongue into my mouth, a thing she had never done before, but which made me clasp her to my bosom with a convulsive energy that seemed to surprise her. For, placing her hand into my lap for an instant, she reddened still more deeply and tore herself free.

'Now that will do, cheri, you are growing naughty, you'll spoil your robe; now stand perfectly still while I remove it carefully'.

I stood still—no, not still, for I was quivering all over—and she untied my garments as quickly as she could with her trembling fingers, for she seemed as much moved as I.

When I was dissolved of all except the chemise and drawers, she clasped me tightly about the waist, then suddenly rose and said in a husky voice: 'You can do the rest yourself, mon cher Henri, I have to hurry downstairs to see a lady who is expecting me to dine with her. Au revoir'.

She left me wondering what was the cause of the sudden change in her. During the ten days which elapsed before the ball, I did not see her, alone—she busied herself all that time with my sisters' dresses. On the morning of the great day she met me in the hall and whispered: 'The gloves and shoes have come, cheri,' and ran off before I could answer.

In pursuance with our agreement, I went to her room to dress. My sisters had been crazy to know what I should wear, but I had kept my secret as I had promised.

When I entered the room, I found Madelon entirely dressed, just putting the finishing touches to her hair.

'Oh, how mean,' I said, 'I wanted to help you'.

'Why didn't you come sooner?'

'But I am on time'.

'Are you? I think not,' she replied with her roguish smile.

'Mon cheri, you can tie bows on my slippers. I've left that for you'. I sat myself on the floor and she placed her dainty feet in my lap. Oh, what perfect little things they were, what delicious ankles, what high insteps and then the fascinating curves of the legs, the lower part of which I could only see. As I tied the ribbons, I raised the dainty foot and kissed it.

'Mon Dieu, how you progress,' she said.

She wore the bosom covered with her white kerchief, naturally, because I had not the same development in that region she had and I was much disappointed, for I had counted on letting my hand burn with delight once more. When she dressed me, she was very careful not to do those delicious, titillating things which had before set me ablaze. And when I asked her why she didn't and said how much I enjoyed them, she leaned back and laughed heartily.

'Do you think I want you to spoil these beautiful dresses which I have put up especially for the occasion?'

But just as the work was finished, she made me put my hands behind my back and then, bending over, gave me another of those wonderful kisses with her magic tongue which had so convulsed me before.

It isn't necessary to say anything much about the ball. We had a glorious time. We had the men about us all the time and they were constantly taking us one for the other. They soon recognized Madelon by her accent, but as I imitated that, they could not tell which was the true Française. Some of the men hugged me awfully tightly when dancing, and some rubbed their legs against mine as if by accident.

The result of all this was that I was in a state of exultation almost bordering on insanity. At the appointed time, just before the unmasking, Madelon and I stole out of the Ballroom and met at her door. She had removed her mask, and her face was aflame. As soon as the door was closed and locked on me, I flung my arms about her neck and kissed her in the thrilling manner she had so lately taught me. As I did so, she abandoned herself in my arms and closed her eyes.

'Ah! mon cheri, m'aimes-tu?' she sighed faintly.

'Je t'aime de toute mon ame!' I replied, repeating the kiss which endured for a blissful eternity. I felt that I desired nothing but to hold that exquisite woman and die in her arms, smothered by her perfumed breath. At last she tore herself away from my embrace and staggered to a chair by the window, pressing her hands upon her heaving bosom. The windows at the piazza were all closed tight, but those at the end of the house were wide open and the moonbeams streamed into the room, making it shimmer with their silvery light.

'Leave me, leave me, Henri, you must leave me,' she faltered as I went to her and laid my hands on hers.

'Why, how can I undress myself?' I replied. What could be the matter with her? This was the second time she had acted so and I couldn't make it out. Not knowing what to do, I put my arm about her waist and gazed into her beautiful eyes.

'What have I done, chère Madelon? It makes me feel dreadful to think that I may have hurt you—when I do love you so much'.

She looked at me for a time, saying nothing—with the strangest look on her face; it seemed as though one thought after another were chasing across it. Then she smiled a wonderful smile and said in a whisper:

'Je t'aime, oh! je t'aime, mon Henri, yes, you may stay,' and with this she wound her arms about my neck and drawing my face down, pressed it against her burning cheek.

For some time we remained motionless. I had sunk to my knees before her. She passed her thrilling hands through my hair, disarranging the elaborate coiffure and making the false hair fall to the floor, but likewise disarranging my whole internal being in which a conflagration had been blazing that would have done honour to Moscow. She thrust her hand into my bosom, pulled out the chest protectors and threw them away.

'Those horrid stiff things are only in the way!' she whispered, pushing back my hair and kissing me at the spot where the neck joins the chest—a long clinging kiss—a kiss which had the result of giving me a most delicious inspiration. In my turn, I quickly pulled out the pearl pin which fastened her neckerchief and, throwing it back, exposed to the gaze of my dazzled eye and to the tender moon the divinest bosom I have ever seen. Imagine two soft but fine snowy elevations, perfectly shaped, rising and falling rapidly as Madelon's breath came more quickly. Just above the edge of the lace-trimmed chemise appeared two rosy points, a little raised as if inviting a kiss, and between them a most mysterious passage, leading down—down to what I found out afterwards was paradise.

I drew a deep sigh of delight and desire and buried my face between them in that perfumed mysterious passageway—then I kissed them passionately, taking the rosebuds between my burning lips. I was perfectly innocent, as you may suppose, of the ultimate purpose of all this. All that I knew was that it thrilled me with a most delicious comfort and consumed me with a burning desire to see more of the exquisite body which was rapidly intoxicating me.

Madelon leaned back as if in a faint, her warm hands about my neck, abandoning her lips, her throat and her bosom to my kisses, while from below came the thrilling music of the dance, which alone was enough to keep us from regaining our senses. Filled with my new desire, I began unpinning her.

'Oh, how naughty you are,' she laughed nervously. 'What do you want?'

'I don't know; I guess I'm crazy, Madelon, ma chère. But I want to see more of you, you are so beautiful!'

'Keep your mischievous hands from me,' she faltered and seized my hands in hers. For a moment I thought she was going to escape as before; she looked at me with such a strange expression, a look in which doubt, confidence, terror and desire were intermingled. I see now that at that moment my fortune hung in the balance. A happy inspiration flashed into my mind!

'Oh, Madelon! I'll die if you don't love me, love me, my soul'. And then I drew her to me and pressed my lips to hers. Our tongues met, sending a nameless thrill through me that nearly took away my senses.

It must have affected her, too, for she fell back in the chair and offered no resistance to my proceedings. After a moment, she also busied herself with the pins and hooks of my attire. In the course of my feverish work, a certain string got tied into a hard knot.

'Tear it! Tear it! Henri,' she cried frantically. 'Never mind, tear anything!'

Then sinking at her feet, I flung her dainty slippers across the room and, reaching up under her perfumed skirts, quickly removed her garters and black silk stockings, revealing the snowy feet I had so much longed to see. Oh, how I kissed them, stroked them and placed them at my bare breast, feeling the touch of the delicate toes like wanton flames burning their way into my heart.

Then with a wild, frantic laugh, she rose—raising me likewise to my feet.

'Tear off your clothes, Henri—rip them if necessary'. When I emerged from the tangle of white drapery in which I was involved, I saw her standing before me in her adorable nudity, her hair loose and falling over her shoulders, her perfectly modelled arms outstretched, inviting me. How can I describe the wonder of the vision illuminated by the moonlight sharply outlined against the shadows of the room?

The wonderful curve of the hips and thighs, the perfect modelling of the knees and ankles; the marvel of the fully disclosed breasts completed by the entrancing region below the mysterious navel and the little hill with its delicate shrubbery which fenced all these beauties into one location, the intoxicating centre. How it was, I know not, but my delicious gaze fastened there. For some time I looked motionless, almost breathless. Had I thought of looking at myself, I might have seen a notable change in my own anatomy, but such a thing never entered my head.

'Come, Henri, my love! Come,' she gasped. I fell into her arms, we clasped each other in a convulsive embrace and staggered to the bed. For some time we lay there motionless. I must have lost consciousness for a moment, for all I remember is something like awakening from a dream, feeling the pressure of her fine bosom against my breast, the tight embrace of arms and thighs, the touch of her quivering tongue within my lips, the music of the dance, which seemed to come from an indefinite distance.

Then I became aware of something hard and rigid between my legs, which were pressing against hers, throbbing violently, a something which hurt but thrilled me. It was darker where we were and from amidst the dusk I could feel her deep eyes searching the very depth of my being—I had no desire to move, I wanted to die, to die of these delights.

'Oh, mon Henri! Mon Henri! Don't you know anything?' she gasped at last.

'Nothing, except that I am in heaven,' I replied, kissing her again.

'Then Henri, do just what I show you! Kiss me, kiss me deep'.

She rolled upon the bed, pulling me over her, then unclasped one hand and reached down, grasping that strange rigid thing which I mentioned before, sending a shock over my body that made me thrust my tongue far down between her delicious lips. And then I felt that hitherto unknown part of me sinking slowly but surely into her burning body as, pressing her feet against my thighs, she drew me in.

The place was tight and the hot, moist flesh closed around me with a clinging kiss as her lips did on mine, drawing the soul from me. What was this new and wonderful sensation? Could there be anything more?

'Oh Henri, mon Henri, move a little, just a little, back and forth, slowly—softly—Oh mon Dieu, mon Dieu!'

'Madelon, Madelon, my love, what are you doing? You are killing me!'

'Yes, yes, I am killing you, cheri, but kill me, too! Vite, vite, plus vite—as fast as you can—faster—faster—harder—harder yet. Don't spare me. Squeeze me to death! Henri! Henri! your tongue! Ah, I am dying.'

It seemed as though cords of flame were all over my body from the roots of my hair to the tips of my toes, and as if these cords were knotted in that mysterious member inside of her and that something in her had tight hold of the knot and was drawing my blood, my nerves, my life, my soul, out of me. With a convulsive clasp she gave a smothered cry, seized my shoulder in her pearly teeth, and bit it sharply, then fell back fainting. I did not feel any hurt then, for just at that moment something burst with a thrill of pleasure so keen as to be a positive pain. It was as though I was bleeding to death and with a deep sigh, I fell forward breathless. When I gathered my scattered senses together. I heard the dance music, as though coming from a distance, grow louder, louder, and then I became conscious of her delicious body heaving, panting under mine and I felt a sharp pain in my shoulder. I gazed into her face. In the dim light I could see her eyes open slowly with a look of unutterable love. I was afraid that the weight of my body might hurt her, and so tried to rise, but, clasping me once more in her divine arms and thighs, she held me close and murmured faintly.

'Henri! Henri! If you leave me now I shall never love you anymore!' It is needless to say that I stayed. It was dawn when I crept back to my room. The dance was over and the inmates of the hotel were wrapped in heavy slumber. I had learned my delicious lessons, lessons which I have never seen equalled since.

For the remainder of the summer, I often made my way by the piazza into my Madelon's window and my mother was much surprised at the fact that, whereas in the beginning of the summer I had been so strong and ruddy, I had towards its close in spite of the bracing mountain air, grown pale and thin, with dark rings about my eyes.

Madelon's husband was recalled that autumn; she went with him and I have never seen her since, except in my luxurious dreams.

Letters from Three Maids

HE title of this late Victorian example of the pornographic novel (c. 1887) only partly represents the contents which are wholly comprised of exchanges of outrageous letters between the members of a family of four together with others from aunts and cousins, and the occasional intervention of the author from the wings. The total effect is of a slightly romanticized version of *The Romance of Lust* in epistolary form. As in that much longer novel, the romanticized Victorian concept of the family is inverted and perverted in the manner and intent of later soi-disant 'protest' literature of our own time.

CHAPTER ONE

Dearest Reader, if you are discomforted from revelations of intimacy, then I must beg you to read no further in this volume which you have now to hand. For we have here presented nothing more nor less than the most intimate of exchanges between certain persons, so intimate that they have indeed been held secret all these years from any save the very individuals most concerned, and have not even been seen by such close associates as husbands, mothers, and such. But in order that you may understand in the rightest manner the workings of the heart and particularly the ways of romance, which are a complicated business at best, we have produced for discreet perusal these documents, being written messages after the manner of love letters. They shall demonstrate certain facts for us, which we shall quickly point out as they are represented.

Most especially, we shall attempt to make clear one point which comes to the heart of it: in short, that all lovers are hypocrites, for such is the nature of the game. All things being permissible in romance, as they are in battle, this is not so heinous a crime, and these ruses may be observed with tolerance when they occur in another's romance, or with amusement when they occur in our own. Only he need be perturbed who finds no such deceit within his affairs, for it is certain either that he is unloved, or too well deceived.

But let us on to our letters, which speak in some degree for themselves. We need but concern ourselves somewhat with the characters in our little play, whom we shall meet promptly. Of these the first, who raises our curtain in a manner of saying, can be said to be our hero, albeit he will not fit the mould too oft portrayed in lore. He is nonetheless a handsome creature, not yet twenty by a full two years, so that he combines that sweet freshness of the lad, that bloom still lingers, with the lusty appeal of the man, this combination being one that has throughout the centuries led otherwise virtuous creatures astray and shattered good hearts with irresistible appeal.

Our Randolph, for such is this dashing creature's name, sports dark locks that frame his angelic face. He stands comfortably tall, and lean of frame, and has been generously supplied by a nature of those members which quicken the hearts of lustful women.

As to his manner of behaving, especially as concerns matters of romance, well, we shall see that for itself, in those letters of which we earlier spoke. And here are three, all to ladies; indeed, to members of his family, these being his cousin, his aunt, and his sweet young sister.

Dear reader, we shall leave you to see for yourself what manner of lover and family member is our young Randolph. He shall tell you, as it were, in his own words. But we beg you, repeat them not, for they were told in confidence, and were not meant for general circulation, since were they to be gotten about the city, they might cause some considerable embarrassment to certain persons who, by the nature of their descriptions herein, might too easily be identified.

My dearest Cousin Abagail,

How I have missed you these past three weeks since retiring to the country. While in truth it is pleasant to be away from London for this brief respite, I confess that I should happily endure all of that discomfort in order to be with you but for one more night. I am a man, as you know, who poorly endures these abstinences from pleasure; and indeed, to be away from you is truly to be gone from pleasure. Have no fears, though, on the question of my fidelity, for I shall put you utterly at ease on that subject. I own that, as I left the city, I thought fleetingly that perhaps I should resort to taking sport—though certainly less pleasant sport than I enjoy with you—elsewhere, and that I in fact cast my eyes about once or again with the object in mind of finding some harmless country lass all too eager to satisfy any physical cravings that I might suffer. Alas, I saw several who were at first inspection sweet enough, considering that they were only rustic creatures and without the city's refinements. But in each instance, there appeared before me suddenly a vision of you in your full glory, with golden tresses fanned across your pillow, with the milky whiteness of your breasts rising and falling with your breathing, your gentle thighs trembling as I stroke them. So heady has this vision been that, fairly swooning with the delicious agony of remembering you, I have then looked upon these country lasses as though they were veritable beasts of burden, utterly lacking in charm or beauty. So I have been completely faithful to you, my beloved cousin and shall remain so, despite my lusty ways, with which you are familiar, for I have no alternative. And I trust too that you shall remember your vows to me, and let no other partake of those delicious treasures which I have come to consider my very own, and without which I should surely die, for life would have no value to me should I lose my beloved Abagail ...

Until I am able to return to you, then, I shall somehow endure this lonely agony, gathering my strength solely from those all too rare and infrequent messages which come from you in the post, and which I read over and over, savouring every word and every unwritten sigh ...

Your enchanted cousin,
Randolph

My Dearest Aunt Gwendolyn,

Words alone cannot suffice to tell you the joy I experienced upon receiving your all too brief epistle, telling me that you did after all still care for me, if only a light bit. Could you but have known, it came but scarcely in time to save the life of this worthless nephew of yours, for I had decided to be done with it, since it had lost its value having, I thought, lost you ...

Oh, the agony of knowing that you are in Cornwall, so distant, and with your husband, so that there is no hope of a reuniting, not for a fortnight or better. Would that you were in London, so that I could fly to you, shower you with kisses enough to prove that love I feel for you and which you so mistakenly question. Then would I suck at those ruby berries that adorn your breasts, and kiss that silken bower lower where I have worshipped you so eagerly.

But it is not enough to know that you care for me only a slight bit; I confess, I thought that you cared more, although I could never ask you to love as I do, for there has never been so great a love, so complete an adoration, as that which I feel for you, my angel. But love me you must, for if you sincerely do not, then I shall carry through with my plans, and take my life, but if I thought that you truly did care about it, then I shall remain alive, but unhappy until you have come to me. Thus do I put myself completely into your delicate hands, those loveliest of hands, so that you can see there are no bounds to my love.

You ask if I have found for myself a playmate to entertain myself with whilst in the country. How my heart ached at those words, at the very thought that you could expect such of me. Indeed, I will not question that I have had a reputation in the past of being a wild boyo. But that was when I was a boy, and I am a man now, our love having channelled that, so that I find it impossible to be even polite to a member of your sex, since invariably she must face comparison to you, the result of which is that she becomes odious to me. Indeed, it is certainly fortunate that my mother and my sweet sister are themselves travelling, leaving my father and I to ourselves, for even their company, once beloved to me, rankles now . . .

Oh, my darling, my beloved Aunt, you must know to what depths of unhappiness I have sunk since our quarrel, and since I left London that following day, and was unable to see you to repair the damage we had done. I fear that this letter is but little lucid, for my mind fails me, and my sight is hampered by the rivers of tears that have streamed from my sorry eyes. I beg of you, forgive me completely, permit me to correct whatever mistaken impressions you have formed, and let us again take up our passionate romance which meant such happiness for me.

Your desperate nephew,
Randolph

My Dearest Sister Louisa,

How delighted was I to receive your letter, since it told me not only that you and our mother had reached Paris safely on your holiday, but moreoever, offered those sweet words to my ears; for I confess, it was a joy to me to know how unhappy you are on this accursed journey which has separated us, if only for a few weeks. But it is such a crucial time, having so recently discovered the true depth of the love which we feel for one another, which goes far beyond that pale affection common to brothers and sisters and which I late thought was all that existed between us. Oh, how I remember that night—was it only this summer—when I came unannounced into your chamber and found you not, as I had expected, fully garbed, but rather standing in that magnificent unclothedness with which I have since been haunted. My beloved, you know that I have been wicked in the past, for I confess to you all my doings, as you confess yours to me. But I say in all honesty, I feel that all those other maids were but a prelude to you, a preparation that would thus enable me to fully appreciate all that you had to offer, and that would entrain me to better provide you with the pleasure which you so richly deserve.

My beloved, I can understand that you have been and will

continue to be quite deluged with temptations, for you are away from me, who could satisfy those lusty urges which seem common to our blood; and you are with our mother who, we both know, is a woman of nearly unchecked licentiousness, despite the air of gentility which she affects, and I do not think that we could enumerate the men she has had right here in her husband's (and our father's) home. So you will no doubt have that to contend with as well, and too, you are in a land where men have not courtesy toward a lady of refinement, but think only of bedding her, so that a creature of your loveliness will be set upon at every minute.

But I pray you, not to succumb, for while I sympathize with your unhappiness, for indeed I suffer the same lusty urges, and perhaps stronger, which is the way with me, but I have for your own dear sake restrained them, and have kept my vow to be faithful. Indeed, did I not come down here from London, to remove myself from all temptation? Therefore be firm, and we shall recompense one another for this period of restraint when we are again joined, for which moment alone do I live.

Your impatient brother,
Randolph

H

Rosa Rogers

osa Rogers, or the Romance of a Country Girl told by Herself in Letters to a Friend (c. 1898) is an exceedingly rare book, of which—initially at least—only 100 copies were printed. The imprint, 'Privately printed for Subscribers only by the Cunnusberg Society, Harvard, U.S.A.' is, naturally, false though the book was almost certainly printed in America. The volume of 132 pp carries a terminal announcement of the 'next publication': *Lady Rodwell; a Nurserymaid's Tale of Flagellation Up-To-Date*.

Rosa Rogers is a little literary horror clothed in the prettiest typographical raiment. The title page—a small work of art by any typographer's standards—is in two colours, the margins are generous, the imposition poor, the layout and setting excellent.

The story is a mish-mash of adolescent events told in letters. So barely does it reach the level of literacy, that the suspicion obtains —in view of the excellent production—that the author was also the proud publisher. The book is undoubtedly memorable for several phrases indicative of the author's moronic mentality. 'My dear old Dad it makes me come' is perhaps his classic.

Rosa Rogers

LETTER IX

Dear Frank,

After Alfred was gone, Suzette brought us some tea, then undressed her young mistress and prepared her for bed, and when I thought myself of retiring, Miss L—— said 'Oh not quite yet Rosie dear, are you a good reader?'

'My teacher at school said I was the best reader in her class, but we only had goody-goody books there; if you let me try I will do my best'.

'I get some funny letters from the fellows I know, and have a rare collection of books (regular snorters, as the Americans would say) which you will have to amuse me with, when I am dull or done up; now look in that escritoire and you will see a letter from dear old Willie Norton who is in Paris, and promised to send me his adventures'.

The letter was written in a clear style on many sheets of paper.

'Oh dear Miss, do you expect me to go through all that this evening'.

'Well that all depends whether it is very spicy or not, now go on dear'.

It was as follows:
My Fucking Princess,

I am going to redeem my promise and relate a lark, or rather larks which have happened to me, but please excuse my way of relating the incidents, you know I shall be the real hero, but I want to tell the story as if it happened to a student years ago.

A young man left the Quartier Latin, he wore the peculiar devil-may-care dress, the long pointed beard, the full cloak, and the broad brimmed hat, which from the beginning of time have characterized the Student of Paris.

Silently and carefully he passed along, saying nothing to the many who strode beside him, yet one who observed carefully might have seen, that he looked beneath the bonnet of every pretty woman, grisette or other who chanced to meet him. A careful observer might also have seen, that many pretty women looked behind them, as if to catch one glance of a person, who certainly by name at least was not unknown to them. The gazer, and the person on whom all gazed, was one well-known in Paris, Charles de Beauguard,

115

representative of one of the noblest families of France, yet an American.

Many pretty women passed by, all of them looked into Charles' face, but not one turned either to the right or the left, until having passed half the city, our hero stood at the corner of the Rue de Rivoli. Waiting a little while, a young girl came from beneath the Arcade in front of the Ministry of Finance, and asked, 'is it you, Monsieur Charles?'

'Yes, darling, it is I' was the reply.

'Come with me, she expects you,' at her orders away they went, we will not attempt to follow them, to say what streets they crossed, what alleys they passed, what the gendarmes said, or how at last they arrived at not a bad-looking house in one of the small streets bisecting the Rivoli, or how Monsieur Charles was introduced into the *salle à manger* of M. Julien Lorgnet, the doyen of the faculty of advocates, a man of forty-five or fifty, somewhat *blasé*, and anxious only to speak what he thought to the *cour de cassation* without the slightest recollection that Mlle. sat at home wondering why he did not attend to his own family, and why the *cour de cassation* was of more importance than herself—how M. Lorgnet was much to be pitied: he had a pretty wife whom he neglected for a maid to whom he paid more attention. Monsieur De Beauguard was, however, of more importance, and liable to more annoyance, for he had taken the responsibility, not only of making love to the maid, but to the young mistress also.

As he went home with the pretty grisette, he invited her to put her arm beneath his, and as they walked down the Rue de Rivoli more than once the tips of his fingers strayed into the palm of her hand—what he meant by that titillation is more than the writer can explain. It must have been an invitation to do something wrong, from the fact that more than once she said, 'now don't,' 'have done,' 'away with you,' etc.

At last she showed Charles into a comfortably furnished room on the first floor, a night key let them in, and Charles found himself surrounded by a harp, piano, rack of books, and a thousand little articles of *vertu* demonstrating the taste of the person he had come to see.

'Monsieur,' said the grisette, as she returned from announcing him, 'Mlle. will see you soon, but as her grandmother is paying her a small monthly visit, she bade me sit with you awhile'.

'What a pleasure! Sit by me, my beautiful!' The grisette had rosy cheeks and deep blue passionate eyes, a pale brow and a bust like Juno's. She sat by Charles.

The sofa was one of those large old ones now nearly obsolete— a low back, but the seat was wide, and the ends had exactly the proper angle.

The grisette sat by the side of Charles, and as he looked into her blue eyes a strange sort of feeling came over him which he could not resist. He took her by the hand, pressed it, and strange to say the pressure was returned.

The arm of Charles insensibly was passed around her waist, and the fair grisette laid her full warm cheek and panting bosom on the face and shoulder of the student.

Shame to say, he kissed her, and for more shame, she did not object to return his kisses. They sat closer and closer together, at last their conversation ceased, but one who observed carefully might have found out something from their panting, sighing and what Catullus calls 'tremula quassatioque lecti'. They were silent, but a light and fairy footstep was heard in the hall, the grisette sprang up as if she was shot and disappeared, the next moment Charles was clasped in the arms of her he had come to see.

'Charles! Charles! why have you been so late? How long I waited for you. Good gracious, what is the matter with your ruffles? and your collar is all rumpled, what have you been doing?'

Now the fact was Charles De Beauguard and the pretty grisette had been sitting rather more close together than old persons think young persons have any right to do.

The young lady seemed difficult to pacify. For a long time she would not be persuaded to turn her face towards him, and sat pouting her pretty lips, and rocking most outrageously; Charles attempted to put his arm round her waist, but she would not have it. He seized her fingers, only to have them snatched away, finally he took her by force and though she trembled, fought and struggled, his strength enabled him at last to seat her on his knee.

'Now Charles tell me.'

'Tell you what?'

'How came your linen to be so rumpled?'

'How should I know—when one has so much to do, as I have, it is difficult indeed to keep all right.'

'True—true.'

Shocking to relate, but the forms of the couple gradually lost their upright position and sank, sank, sank, until our Lothario was engaged in an operation to which the young lady's mama never would have consented—now what was the circumstance, and what the story of the young couple so guiltily engaged?

Charles De Beauguard was the son of an old colonel of cavalry, who having become fully aware of all the dangers of the army and military life—aware of the fact that most regiments are on the footing of that famous English one, where every private has one wife and the adjutant two, had resolved that his son should be brought up otherwise, and therefore pitched upon medicine as his profession.

He sent the young man to Paris, and placed him in the Quartier Latin to keep him out of temptation.

The story is soon told, the young gentleman had a pleasant address, he knew all the ways of the town, and had ended by establishing rather too close an intimacy with the daughter of his professor and guardian. How they met was strange—the old professor had invited the young man home and bade all take particular care of him. The result was, Bernard the butler was particularly deferential, though he had little respect for students—Annette the grisette had been very civil, though she did not like boys, and Mlle. Louise, the daughter, and Annette the grisette, knowing no better, had been rivals.

This was Charles De Beauguard—the history of whom for a day we are about to trace, and all, we think will be amazed at the miracles of adventures of the Parisian Don Juan,

Yours lovingly,

Rosa

Rosa Rogers

LETTER X

Dear Frank,

To resume the story—Charles and the young girl sat together, the aversion she had first manifested to sitting on his knee was gone, and now with her head on his shoulder, with her long hair streaming over his back, and her bust, gleaming in the half-obscurity of the room like two globes of marble, she seemed to luxuriate in the caresses of which he was so prodigal—who can tell or repeat what young people say in this situation? How uninteresting it would be to record that he thought her eyes brighter than diamonds, her teeth like pearls, her hair like the raven's wing, and assured her how beautiful he thought her form.

The latter, indeed, we can believe, for if ever a man heaped caresses on an idol, Charles did like Louise—the marble statue Pygmalion made and worshipped was nothing to it—she lay in the hollow of his arm; she nestled in his bosom, and the most accurate timepiece would not have distinguished the difference of a second in the vibration of their hearts—her lips grew moist, her eyes swam in water, her cheeks became suffused, and once and anon a tremor passed over her frame, as if she were unable to restrain her emotions, which would find vent.

Poor girl! yet why pity her? She was then in the happiest moments of her life. She yielded her whole soul to the intoxication of that madness, so pleasant and yet so much abused—she surrendered everything to one she loved, and received in return a bliss, more exquisite than anything even Heaven itself can offer. Who can tell, even had she been called on to atone by a life of suffering for this half-hour of pleasure, that too high a price would have been paid for it.

'Oh, Charles,' said she, 'can we not live thus always? My father and your own are friends; speak to him and he will not refuse us happiness—do so, dear Charles, do so!' He stopped that delicate mouth with kisses—he passed his arm yet further round her waist, and pressed her yet closer to his bosom. Perforce she could say nothing, and consented like Esau for a mess of pottage, to part with that woman's birthright, a husband's love. Other people may think Charles a villain—so passed the early part of the night, alternate caresses and slumber, and the twain were beginning to discuss the propriety of parting or remaining together for the night. Just then

119

a step was heard at the door, and Louise said, 'oh, it is my father,' immediately hurrying Charles into a kind of wardrobe, half-way between two rooms, and making a passage practicable between them—while there he saw sights—in the next room was the fair grisette, lolling in delicious *negligé*, while beside her lay one of his fellow-students, whose panting and convulsive breathing proved him to have been employed at some laborious occupation—a more decided evidence was however afforded by his dress, and the profusion of fine linen visible, not precisely where it is customary to display it. The scene was not a pleasant one for Charles, men do not like to see their fellows thus engaged. It is not agreeable, for after all, the flesh will rise. Thus ensconced our hero again and again saw the play rehearsed. At last in a high state of excitement he was recalled by Louise. Flying into her arms, with all the impetus of passion, there is no knowing what might have been the result, had not the father's step been again heard in the *rez de chaussé*. He was at once put out into the balcony, and left to shift for himself.

Next door to the house of Louise's father was a devout and pious Abbé, idolized by all the women of his charge, on account of his parental and holy conduct—some strange things were however then going on his house.

The night was clear and starlight, so that objects could be seen almost as well as by daylight, consequently when Charles opened the garden gate, he saw distinctly the flutter of a white robe at the priest's door. Now it is well-known that in France the alb is not worn in the streets, and the only conclusion to the drama was that some fair penitent made a midnight confession to the father.

The church was next to the house, and seeing a light flash on the wall, Charles determined at once to discover who was the penitent that had such a weight of sin on her soul, as to be forced at night to hurry and lay the burden down. I am afraid our hero did very wrong in this, it is always indiscreet to pry into a lady's secrets, it must, however, for his excuse be remembered that he was very young and a student, and therefore with a roving commission to do as he pleased as long as he lived in the Quartier Latin.

Going as near to windows as possible he could see that the lady had taken off her bonnet, that she was fair and buxom, and contrary to his expectation she had come, not to receive, but to administer consolation, for the Abbé knelt before her, bestowing the kiss of the church, not on her forehead but on two voluptuous, passionate looking lips, which seemed nothing loth to receive his osculation, whilst the busy hands strayed up and down over her bosom, which seemed full and hard as if it were of marble.

What was the result of this adventure I cannot tell, for the Abbé rose and drew down the curtain, and Charles could only see them cross the room towards a sofa, which he knew stood at the other end of it.

Until then he had fancied that with Annette and Louise he had committed a great sin. He now, however, began to reflect, and came to the conclusion that what so excellent a man as the Abbé had done could not be wrong, and that he had perhaps done something commendable. Sure it is, that he experienced not a little relief therefrom. We have, of course, no means of ascertaining these adventures, having happened to him, not myself.

They, however, demonstrated an important fact, that priests of all denominations have much to do, that the public know nothing of, which may account for the pale emaciated air of many of them.

The light at last disappeared from the window of the room, and stepping aside Charles saw the lady come from the door, making an appointment to come again to visit the priest after Vespers on the next Sunday. The door was closed, and the buxom fair one passed rapidly down the street, our gay student in full pursuit. He overtook her, for women never fly except to be overtaken, and frankly and without prelude told the story of what he had seen. This again was very wrong of Charles, but he was a wild harum-scarum student and thought of nothing but the gratification of the passion, always the most prominent in youths of his age. After the lapse of some minutes confusion they arrived at the lady's house, and as she persisted in denying what had occurred, there was no difficulty as to matters of conversation.

The lady persisted in denial—Charles in affirmation, and after a conversation of some minutes at the door, the servant who opened it, a very discreet soubrette, having in the interim assured her that her husband had gone to attend on a lady on the occasion of her accouchment (she was a Doctor's wife), our hero was invited in to discuss the question at liberty.

Heretofore, we have been able to give but a bird's-eye view of the lady's charms, now, however, we can be more descriptive. She was thirty-six, an age many think the most attractive, her complexion was bright as it had ever been, and her bust had acquired that full voluptuousness compared with which the bosom of a younger woman is but petite and uninteresting, as she crossed a brilliantly lighted room, a trim, yet full ankle might have been seen, and a tournure sufficiently developed to have entranced a Hercules. They sat on the sofa together, talked of all imaginable things, until gradually getting closer and closer, we are constrained to add that something quite as extraordinary as what happened in the priest's house took place between them.

Now good bye, perhaps I shall have another yarn to send you in a few days.

'I think you may as well retire now, dear, it is a neat pretty story, only I so much prefer outspoken words,' said my mistress.

And I like her taste, don't you, my dear Frank? With same old love.

Rosa

The Voluptuous Night

he *Voluptuous Night, or the No Plus Ultra of Pleasure* is of sufficiently curious provenance to include here, although it falls earlier than the stated period of this anthology. It derives from a translation of one of the many obscene and libellous pamphlets that were written against Marie Antoinette*—a translation which the compiler or editor refers to obliquely in a prefacing 'Advertisement':

> In a French work, printed at Rome, under the title of 'Bibliotheque Erotique', there is a well-written tract called 'La Nuit Merveilleuse', which many persons have been desirous of seeing in an English dress. To accommodate that class of public, the Translator has undertaken the task, and flatters herself they will find it executed with spirit and fidelity.

This note is signed by Mary Wilson, whose name also appears on the title page over the date of 1830: *Printed by Sarah Brown, Princes Place, Pimlico.*

Mary Wilson is a slightly mysterious person. She, or whoever used the name, operated as a publisher and part author in the second

---

* See *The Slandered Queen* by Dudley Leslie (Robert Gordon, London, 1971).

and third decades of the nineteenth century, and a note on her is found in an edition of *The Exhibition of Female Flagellants* (c. 1830), printed 'for the benefit of Mary Wilson', with the following note by one Theresa Berkley who allegedly bore the cost:

> To my personal friends, I need not explain the cause of Miss Wilson's difficulties, as they are well acquainted with her misfortunes, and will, I am sure, patronize this work which I have caused to be reprinted for her benefit. To those who are unacquainted with Miss Wilson, I beg leave to state that she is the Reviver of Erotic Literature in the present century. When she commenced her career there was but one good book in the market, 'The Woman of Pleasure' (*Fanny Hill* - Ed.). She herself edited, or translated twelve different works: her success has stimulated others to embark in the same line of useful exertion, and we have now upwards of fifty volumes of Voluptuous Entertainments for the Rising Generation.

We are unlikely now, ever to know whether Mary Wilson ever existed—a unique example of a woman publisher of pornography—or if the name was assumed as a veiling hoax. Ashbee notes several 'portraits' of her; if she did not exist, she was decidedly well launched as a 'brand name'. *The Voluptuous Night,* itself of only sixty-nine pages, and in which Marie Antoinette figures as 'Madame Terville', is followed by *The Whore's Catechism,* another evident translation, and a poem—*The Frozen Limb*—which is added for mere measure.

CHAPTER ONE

At the decease of my father, I came into the uncontrolled possession of a fortune which, though moderate, was yet sufficient to
gratify my limited desires. That part of it which consisted of landed
property, comprised, among other valuable estates, the ancient
hereditary baronial domain of Bellesfesses, celebrated alike for
fertility of its soil, the beauty of its scenery, the extent of its territory
and the unbounded hospitality of its lords.

Three or four magnificent hotels at Paris, with about £400,000
in the funds, and £60,000 in ready cash at my bankers, constituted
the remainder of my inheritance.

I was then but just turned of three-and-twenty. Weary of what
appeared to my youthful and ardent mind the insipid monotony of
a country life, I resolved to hasten to Paris, there to pursue the
path of pleasure, ambition, or glory.

My reception at Court was highly gracious. The Monarch was
pleased to eulogize the loyalty and bravery of my distinguished
ancestors, and especially to pass strong encomiums on the fealty and
merits of my late father.

'That I may have the pleasure, sir,' continued his Majesty, 'of
frequently seeing near me the representative of a friend I so highly
esteemed, I appoint you to a Captaincy in my Body Guard'.

A reception so flattering, and an appointment that gave me immediate access to the Court and the highest circles, at once determined my wavering resolves.

Requesting, therefore, my banker to provide me with an establishment, I boldly entered the vortex of fashion and of pleasure.

Young, gay, of happy constitution, with an athletic yet sym-
metrically proportioned person—endowed with a lively imagination,
having a reasonable share of good sense and good nature, tempered
by as much knowledge as the generality of the best educated young
men of that day, possessed with a disposition that led me always to
do everything to please, and to abstain from everything that might
offend those with whom I came in contact—I was esteemed and
respected by men, and adored by the women.

Though there was scarcely any enjoyment beyond my reach, and
although I tasted of pleasure in all its varied forms, yet the strongest
penchant of my mind was to the delights that are derived from an
amiable and intimate intercourse with the fair sex—the pleasures

resulting from the lively and unrestrained discourse of a young, handsome and virtuous female, and the raptures experienced in the enjoyment of her person.

To these pleasures I was constitutionally biased, and by nature eminently gifted. They formed the ruling passion of my mind. My whole soul was indeed centred in them; and I permitted no opportunity of discreetly enjoying them to escape me.

Neither grossly and indiscriminately promiscuous, nor absurdly fastidious in my amours, the woman of fashion, the waiting maid, or the washerwoman, provided only that they possessed youth, beauty, and that happy plumpness of person and rotundity of limbs usually denominated *embonpoint,* were all equally loved, courted, and enjoyed by me.

Women in all ranks of life were adored by me; and frequently when lifting the cambric chemise of a marchioness, or the calico jupe of a milliner have I, as I intently surveyed the centre of bliss, dropped on my knees, and covering it with burning kisses, exclaimed, as I affectionately and tenderly compressed it with my hand:

> 'All glorious Cunt! through every land and clime,
> Thou reignest omnipotent, eternal, sublime!
> Sinner and saint alike thy empire own.
> And kneel uncovered fore thy joyous throne'.

At my time of life, and with these sentiments, it will be easily imagined that I was not often without some love affair on my hands.

Madame d'Arbonne, so celebrated for her wit, beauty, and gallantry, was at that period the leader of the *ton.* A tender *liaison* existed between us; and I used frequently to assist at those delightful reunions which assembled at her house—all the rank, the beauty, and the talent of France.

It was on one of these occasions that I first beheld Madame Terville. She was in the flower of youth, handsome in her person, elegant in her manner, fascinating in her conversation, which, amidst all its gaiety and playfulness, was ever characterized by never exceeding the limits of the strictest propriety and decorum.

It was with surprise I learned her husband was so insensible to her charms that she was in a state of separation. The isolation of her worse than widowhood threw a touching interest around her. My senses also were powerfully influenced by her beauty, yet the delicacy of my sentiments, my connection with Madame d'Arbonne, who was her intimate friend, my aversion to inconstancy, and my knowledge that for a considerable time past a tender friendship had subsisted between her and the young Valsain induced me to stifle the first scintillations of passion, and to regard her only with a cold and decorous politeness.

But I could easily perceive these were not her sentiments. Her eyes perpetually sought mine, and tried, by their soft, penetrating, amorous glances, to read what was passing in my heart, and to reveal to me the state of hers. With this intent, she watched every opportunity of throwing herself in my way; but though her passion for me seemed daily to become more ardent, yet she did not permit it to compromise her dignity, or to infringe on that decorum to which, as will subsequently be seen, Madame Terville was scrupulously attached.

In this position of affairs, it chanced that on my going one evening to Madame d'Arbonne's opera box to await her arrival, I got there so unfashionably early as to put me quite out of countenance, the performance had not even commenced. Scarcely, however, had I entered, when I heard myself called to from the next box. It was the decorous Madame Terville who spoke to me.

'What,' said she 'can bring you here so early? Your time must hang very heavy on your hands. How solitary and lost you seem. Come and sit by me'.

I was far from imagining what extraordinary and romantic events this meeting would give rise to. But in woman that faculty is extremely lively, and Madame Terville instantly conceived a singular project.

'I must,' said she, 'save you from the ridicule which your being seen here so lonely and deserted would bring upon you. I must— the idea is a capital one; and as you are here, there is nothing more easy than for me to execute it. Some propitious deity has conducted you hither. Have you any engagements to-night? If you have, I apprize you that they will not be kept, I shall run away with you. Submit quietly; make no resistance; trust to Providence; call my people. You are a charming, delightful man'.

My entreaties to be excused were of no avail. She compelled me to call her servants. On their appearance:

'Go,' said she to one of them, 'to this gentleman's house, and acquaint his people that he will not be at home tonight'.

She then whispered something to him and dismissed him.

I attempted to speak; but the opera commenced, and she enjoined my silence. We listened, therefore, or at least pretended to listen to the performance. Scarcely however, was the first act over, when a note was handed to Madame Terville, and it was at the same time announced that everything was ready. She smiled, and taking me by the arm, descended to her carriage, caused me to enter it, gave her orders, and we were speedily out of town, without my being able to learn what were her intentions.

Whenever I attempted to question her on the subject, she burst into a loud laugh. If I had not been aware she was a woman of strong passions, and that she had at that very time an avowed attachment of which she could not suppose me ignorant, I should have been tempted to think she meant to make me a happy man.

On her part she was equally well acquainted with the state of my affections, for, as I have already stated, she was the intimate friend of Madame d'Arbonne. I dismissed, therefore, so presumptuous a supposition, and awaited as patiently as I could the *dénouement*.

We changed horses and again pursued our route without a moment's delay. The affair now seemed to be getting rather serious, I then asked, with some earnestness, where this whim of hers would terminate?

'It will terminate,' said she, 'in placing you in a delightful abode —but guess where? I will give you a thousand times to find out. Do you give it up? It is then to my husband's we are going. Are you acquainted with him?'

'Not at all'.

'No matter. I have a slight acquaintance with him, and I think you will like him. We have been reconciled now for these six months and during this month past we have been corresponding with each other. It is, I think very gallant in me to pay him the first visit.'

'It is so, but what, I beseech you, shall I do then? Of what service can I be?'

'That is my business. I dreaded the ennui of a *tête-à-tête*. You are an agreeable companion, and I am delighted at having you with me'.

'But it seems strange that you should choose the day of your reconciliation for my introduction to him. You would make me believe myself a mere cipher, if it was not impossible for a young man of five-and-twenty to be so. Consider also the restraint and embarrassment that always attend a first interview. Truly I see nothing pleasant to any one of us in the scheme you have formed'.

'Bah! no preaching, I beg of you. You mistake your errand. I want you to amuse, to divert, and not preach to me'.

Finding her so determined, I resolved to be equally decided. I began, therefore, to joke about the part I had to act. We became quite gay, and at last her project appeared to me not so very unreasonable.

We changed horses a second time. The mysterious lamp of night illumined a pure sky with a soft voluptuous light. We were approaching the spot where our *tête-à-tête* would finish. She made me at times admire the beauty of the landscape, the calmness of the night, the affecting silence of nature.

To admire this scene more perfectly, we leaned toward the window. In this situation the motion of the carriage caused Madame Terville's beautiful face frequently to come in contact with mine. The most delightful perfume exhaled from her rosy mouth, and thrilled my every vein. A sudden jolt made her grasp my hand; and I wishing to support her in my arms, by the merest accident in the world, placed one of my hands on a breast exquisitely firm and round. Thus reclining on each other, I know not what we looked at. I only remember that objects began rapidly to grow confused to my sight, and that at the delicate and divine lips of Madame Terville.

Suddenly she disengaged herself from me, and threw herself into a corner of the carriage. It was high time, for, to confess the truth the effects of this kiss had begun to work a strange revolution in my whole frame.

'Is it,' said she, after a deep reverie, 'your intention to convince me how imprudent a step I have taken?'

Her question perplexed me.

'My intention—with you—what a mockery! You are too clear-sighted for me to attempt—but accident, surprise—may—be—pardoned'.

'Yes,' replied she, 'you seem to have relied on accident and surprise'.

As we were discussing this point, we entered, without perceiving it, the court-yard of the chateau.

The mansion was illuminated throughout and everything wore the look of joy except the countenance of its proprietor. His languid air plainly evinced that family interests alone induced his reconciliation with his wife. Politeness however caused him to approach the coach door. On my being introduced to him, he offered me his hand, and I followed him into the house, thinking of the part I had to play, and delighted with the subtlety and agility of the mind and person of the beautiful and enchanting Madame Terville, whose charms were disturbing to my imagination and inflaming my blood.

I passed through several rooms, decorated with the utmost taste and magnificence, for the proprietor of the chateau carried luxury to its highest point of refinement, and sought to reanimate the powers of his exhausted constitution by the most attractive and voluptuous pictures. Not knowing what to say, I contented myself with merely admiring them.

The Goddess of the Temple hastened to do its honours, and to receive my compliments.

'You see nothing at present,' said she, 'I must show you the apartment of Monsieur'.

'Ah! Madame,' replied he, 'it is now five years since I unfurnished it'.

'Ha! ha!' returned she, without attending to what she said. I could scarce refrain from laughing when I saw how little she knew of what was passing in her own house.

At supper, she offered to help Monsieur to some pigeon en compote. 'Madame,' replied he, 'I have for these three years confined myself to a vegetable diet'. 'Ha! ha!' said she, again. Imagine to yourself what conversation could take place between three people so surprised to find themselves met together.

Supper over, I expected that we should retire early but my expectation was correct as regarded the husband only. On our return to the drawing room, 'Madame,' said he, 'I feel highly obliged at your having been so provident as to bring this gentleman with you. You thought that I was but a sorry companion for a night's rendez-vous, and you thought rightly, for I shall withdraw'. Then, turning to me, he said, with an air of irony: 'Monsieur will have the goodness to pardon me, and to make my peace with Madame'.

We looked at each other; and to divert the thoughts which this abrupt departure gave rise to, Madame Terville proposed that we should take a turn on the terrace until her people had finished their supper. Nothing could be more agreeable to me! but I dissembled the pleasure I felt, and offering her my arm, conducted to the garden this seducing lady of whom I had already had so delicious a foretaste.

The night was superb. The moon afforded an imperfect light, and seemed to veil objects only to give greater scope to the imagination. The mansion and gardens leaned against a mountain; and the latter stretched their long alleys to the banks of the Seine, which bounded them with its waters, whose numerous windings formed various rural and picturesque islands that diversified the scenery and augmented the beauty of the landscape.

It was in the longest of these alleys that we commenced our promenade. It was overhung with thickly leaved trees. The more we walked, the more forcibly my heart beat. She complained of the manner in which her husband had just been jeering her, and, as we strolled along, confided to me several little secrets. Confidence generates confidence, I entrusted to her several of my secrets, and our conversation became every instant more intimate and more interesting.

She had from the first given me her arm, the rotundity, whiteness, and firmness of which I could not help admiring. By degrees this arm entwined itself with mine until she leant so strongly on me that she scarcely touched the earth. This situation however did not prevent my active fingers from wandering over a breast that with a charming elasticity shrunk from and rebounded to my touch. It was a delightful position, but too fatiguing to be long continued, and we had still a great deal to say to each other.

A green and verdant bank presented itself and we sat down on it without changing our attitude. In this position, which caused me ardently to desire a still more interesting one, we began to extol friendship, and to praise the charms and delights of mutual confidence.

'Ah!' said she to me, 'who can enjoy them better than we, or with less dread of their consequences? I am well aware you are too strongly attached to another person for me to have anything to fear from you'.

Perhaps she wished the contrary, and excited as my desires were, I know not how I remained impassive. My blood was in a boil, I was wild to possess her, and yet I restrained myself. I am myself sincere, and this trait in my character has always caused me to detest affectation and coquettishness in women.

We were thus mutually persuaded that we could never be anything to each other but what we already were. This conviction, however, did not prevent me from surveying the beauties of one of the handsomest bosoms I ever had at my disposal. I endeavoured by gently squeezing two rose buds that delightfully repelled the pressure of my fingers, to awake desire in her palpitating heart.

'I was apprehensive,' said I, 'that my rashness just now in the carriage might have frightened you'.

'Oh! I am not so easily frightened'.

'I fear, however, it has offended you,' and in the meantime, my fingers, as though on the gamut of love, were incessantly playing with her heavenly breasts. 'Can I, by any means, reassure you?'

'It is in your power to do so'.

'In what manner?'

'Can you not guess?'

'But I wish to be told; I want to be certain that you have pardoned me'.

'How shall I convince you?'

'Grant me freely the kiss I accidentally snatched from you, and which appeared to displease you'.

'Why did you not speak plainly? I will grant it to you willingly. My refusal would make you too proud; your self-love would cause you to believe that I was afraid of you'.

She wished to prevent my so deceiving myself, and with that view repeatedly kissed me with ardour.

Heavens! what were my emotions when I felt her delicate tongue, as though darted by Love himself, gently open my glowing lips, insinuate itself like a flash of fire, and seeking my tongue, unite itself with and caress it! No, never can I describe the state into which this amourous and exciting tongue threw all my senses. I thought myself transported to the abodes of the Gods, or that in the Gardens of Imathonté, I was inhaling voluptuousness from the rosy mouth of the most enchanting of the Goddesses.

Kisses are like confidences—they attract, they excite additional ones. In fact, no sooner had she given me the first, than she followed it with a second still more tender—to which a third, yet warmer, succeeded. Our kisses, now mingled together, became so frequent and ardent as to interrupt—to discontinue our conversation, and at last, scarcely did they afford room for our amourous sighs. My breath grew shorter and shorter; the sight—the feel of her swelling breasts, which I covered with repeated and burning kisses—

made me tremble with delight, and thrilled every vein with a gush of ecstatic joy.

A deep silence ensued. We heard it (for silence is sometimes audible). It terrified us. We rose without speaking and resumed our walk—she, disquieted, agitated; I, equally affected, but endeavouring, like Neptune, to calm the tempestuous waves, though my blood was so heated by our mutual caresses, that I could scarcely prevent emitting as we walked.

'We will return,' said she, 'the evening air is unpleasant'.

'I think,' said I, 'it will not affect you'.

'Oh!' replied she, 'I am not susceptible of its influence as many; but that is of no consequence, we will return'.

'It is, doubtless, from regard to me that——. You wish to preserve me from the impressions that a walk like this might make upon me—the fatal consequences to my happiness it might produce'.

'You assign a deal of delicacy to my motives; but I wish to return—I insist on it'.

How awkward is the conversation between two people who compel themselves to talk of every subject except that which they really wish to converse on! She forced me to retake the road of the chateau.

I know not, at least, I did not then know, if in this step she was doing violence to her own feelings, or if it proceeded from her having finally made up her mind, or if she was actuated to it by the mortification she mutually felt at a scene agreeably commenced having terminated so stupidly. However that was, our steps, by a species of instinct, reciprocally became slower, and we walked on, silent, melancholy, and dissatisfied with ourselves and with each other. We knew not how to act. We neither of us had a right to exact—to demand—anything of the other; we could not even have the consolation of mutual reproaches, so that our sentiments were confined to our own breasts. I should have been delighted with a quarrel, but how excite one? Meanwhile we approached the mansion, silently occupied in endeavouring to relieve ourselves from the conditions we had so unskilfully imposed on one another. All that I know is, that in spite of my fine theory on male coquetry I could not imagine how, after what had occurred between us, I could be such a Joseph.

We had reached the fatal door when at last Madame Terville spoke—

'I am not quite satisfied with you. After all the confidence I have shown you, you ought not to have withheld yours from me. During the whole time we have been together, you have not said a single word about Madame d'Arbonne, although it is so delightful to speak of those we love; and you cannot doubt but I should have heard you with interest. I could have done no less than be so complaisant, after having risked depriving you of her'.

'Cannot I reproach you with the same thing? Would not you have pretended much that has occurred if, instead of confiding to me the particulars of your reconciliation with your husband, you have spoken to me of a more suitable subject—of Valsain?'

'A moment's attention, if you please. Think how greatly the slightest suspicion hurts us. The little you know of women ought to make you aware that they will always choose their own time to confide their secrets. But to the point. On what terms are you with Madame d'Arbonne? Are you happy with her? Ah! I fear not; the thought afflicts me, for I feel great interest in your welfare. Yes, Sir, I am interested about you—far more than you may imagine'.

'But why then, Madame, adopt the rumour of a public prone to scandalize, to exaggerate, to invent, and believe that I am intimate with Madame d'Arbonne?'

'Spare yourself the dissimulation. I am thoroughly acquainted with the whole affair. Madame d'Arbonne is not so reserved as you are. Women like always to betray the secrets of their adorers, particularly when like you they maintain a discreet silence which might prevent their conquest being known. I am far from accusing her of coquetry; but a prude has as much vanity as a coquette.

'Tell me candidly, have you not frequently been the victim of this sort of character? Tell me—tell me—'.

'But Madame, you wished to re-enter the château, and the air——'.

'It has changed'.

She took my arm again, and we recommenced our walk, without my noticing what path we took. What she had said of the mistress she was aware I had—what she had said of the lover I knew she had—this journey in which I had met with so many delightful adventures—the scene in the carriage, that on the green bank, the situation, the hour—all these things perplexed me. I was by turns hurried away either by my self-love or by desires, and restored to myself by reflection, but I was too greatly agitated to form any plan or to make any decided resolutions.

Whilst I was thus a prey to contending emotions, she had not ceased speaking an instant; and her discourse ran entirely on Madame d'Arbonne, whilst my silence appeared to confirm everything she thought proper to say of her. Some sentiments which she dropped, recalled me, however, to my senses—or rather to her.

'How artful, but how graceful is she! A treachery in her hands seems nothing but a gaiety; infidelity appears to be an effort of the reason—a sacrifice to decorum; always amiable, rarely affectionate, never true, gallant from disposition, a prude from system—lively, skilful, prudent, rash, sensible, learned—a coquette and a philosopher—she is a Proteus in her forms, and a Grace in her manners —she entices, she eludes. How many parts have I see her play! Between ourselves, with what dupes is she surrounded! What a laughing-stock she has made of Dormeuil; what tricks has she played with Belmont! When she formed a connection with you it was only to confound and mislead them. They had had time to observe her, and would have discovered her real character; to prevent this, she introduced you on the stage, roused their jealousy, excited them to fresh attempts—reduced you to despair, lamented you, consoled you, and finally rendered you all four perfectly contented. Ah! what power has an artful woman over you! and how happy is she, since at the game she has a chance of gaining everything whilst she takes nothing!'

Madame Terville accompanied this last sentence with a most expressive and insinuating sigh. It was a master stroke.

I felt that a bandage had been removed from my eyes, but I did not perceive that it had been replaced by another. My desires which my having carefully restrained them, only caused to inflame me more ardently, completed her triumph. I was struck with the fidelity of the picture she had drawn. Madame d'Arbonne seemed to me the falsest of women. I sighed, though without knowing wherefore, and without discovering whether it proceeded from regret or from hope. She seemed sorry at having disquieted me, and at having allowed herself to go rather too far in a sketch, which, being drawn by a female hand, might very possibly be doubted.

We continued our promenade; and after many ramblings she pointed out to me at the end of the terrace a pavilion that had witnessed our happiest moments. She described to me its situation, and the style in which it was fitted up. What a pity we had not the key! Whilst thus talking we approached it. By accident it was open. Nothing was wanting but daylight; darkness, however, might lend it some attractions. I knew also how heavenly was the object that was about to constitute its principal ornament.

We trembled as we entered. It was a sanctuary and that the sanctuary of love. The God took full possession of our knees—we lost every power and faculty but that of love. Our feeble arms entwined in each other, and we fell involuntarily on a sofa which was placed in a recess of the temple. The moon was on the point of setting, and the last of her rays presently stripped the veil from a modesty that was becoming rather annoying. Darkness confuses and confounds everything. My hands, more impatient than ever, one while roved over two charming globes, smooth and firm as marble, or toyed with albaster thighs, whose softness and plumpness delighted the touch! then they wandered to the centre of pleasure, the entrance to which seemed to be guarded by a profusion of curly hair, only to render it more attractive and exciting to the ardent lover; or played with buttocks whose elasticity, rotundity, and firmness could only be equalled by their fatness, their pliability and their happy adaptation for voluptuousness.

I felt everything—I rummaged everything—I wished to devour everything with my impatient tongue. But a hand repulsed or rather wished to repulse me. Then feeling how forcibly my heart beat she attempted to fly from me, but sank back more agitated, more impassioned than ever. An active and intelligent finger glided opportunely into the pavillion of pleasure, rendered her still more favourable to my wishes. As I titillated her clitoris, her thighs quivered with delight, half opened themselves—every part of her body trembled. I seized the propitious moment, and boldly penetrated to the very bottom of this sanctuary of love. A soft and stifled ejaculation announced her happiness. Her deep drawn sighs—the wild movement of her loins, excited by my skilful fingers—only confirmed what her gestures and her voice had already clearly indicated until at last we sank in that delicious annihilation to which nothing but itself can be compared.

THE FROZEN LIMB

'Twas a cold and frosty night, when her father lay sleeping
  I tapped at the window where Mary was laid,
By the light of her taper I plainly could see her,
  Who's that at the window? she fearfully said,

'Tis I, dearest Mary, both tired and weary,
   I am stiff with the cold, and wet to the skin,
So I pray you take pity and kindly admit me.
   At last she consented, I climbed and stole in.

In bed very quickly my arms did enfold her,
   And tenderly pressing each beautiful charm,
She said I deceived her and falsely had told her
   My limbs were stiff yet she felt them quite warm.
Oh! no, dearest Mary, I did not deceive you,
   I've a limb that is frozen so stiff, dearest maid,
That if you don't lend me your aid to remove it
   I will not be better this night I'm afraid.

She would not believe what I said till she felt it.
   Then, eager to ease the sensation I love,
She offered her own warm bath to melt it,
   Which no one, she told me had bathed in before,
Oh! the warm bath of Mary, so soft and so hairy;
   So delightfully pleasant the entrance lay,
That I'd scarcely been in it much more than a minute,
   When I felt all the stiffness dissolving away.

'Oh Lubin, dear Lubin, you did not deceive me,
   For I felt it now melting so quickly, oh, dear!
That Lubin, dear Lubin, you really must leave me,
   Or I'll die with delight if you longer stop here;
Though the night is so cold and the storm is so dreary.
   Yet heed not the snow, the storm, or the rain.
But if that cold breeze should again your limb freeze,
   Come back to me quickly and melt it again'.

Oh! Mary, these beautiful lips that I'm kissing
   Have more charms for me than the world can bestow,
And this delicate hand I'm so ardently pressing
   Can soon freeze the limb that we melted just now.
She eagerly seized it, and tenderly squeezed it,
   Crying Lubin, dear Lubin, the truth is now plain
For while I keep squeezing your limb keeps fast freezing,
   And now 'tis quite stiff let us melt it again.

We kept melting freezing and Mary kept squeezing
  My sensitive plant all the night till day break,
When at last it quite lost all its power of freezing,
  And Mary, she wondered my limb grew so weak,
Oh! 'tis not surprising, the sun is now rising,
  And all the frost's gone which on last night we found,
But Lubin, this freezing is really so pleasing
  That I wish the snow should last all the year round'.

THE WHORE'S CATECHISM

Question.—What is a Whore?

Answer.—A girl who, having laid modesty entirely aside, no longer blushes at yielding herself to the promiscuous gratification of sensual pleasures with the opposite sex.

Q.—What are the most requisite qualities for a whore to possess?

A.—Impudence, complaisance, and metamorphosis.

Q.—What do you mean by impudence?

A.—I mean that a girl who gives herself up to libidinous commerce should be ashamed of nothing. All parts of her body are to be exposed to the men with as little ceremony as she would expose them to herself, viz., her breasts, her cunt, and her backside, are to be thought no more of when with a strange man whom she has to amuse, than a modest woman of the palm of her hand, which she does not blush to expose.

Q.—What do you mean by complaisance in a whore?

A.—It is an allurement by which she artfully retains the most casual customers. Assuming the air of thorough good nature, she yields herself cheerfully to the various whims, desires, leches, and caprices of men, by which means she retains them as in a net, and obliges them, in spite of themselves, to return another time to the object who has so well gratified a momentary passion.

Q.—What do you mean by metamorphosis?

A.—I mean that a perfect whore should, like the fabled Proteus of old, be able to assume every form, and to vary the attitudes of pleasures according to the times, circumstances, and temperaments. A thoroughbred whore has made her particular study for the various methods of giving pleasure to men for there is a difference between amusing a man of a cold constitution and a man of a warm one—between exciting a vigorous youth and a wornout debauche. Nature, more impressed with the one, requires only to be relieved in the regular way; and, more moderate with the other, requires different degrees of titillation, situations more voluptuous, coaxings and frictions more piquant and more lewd. The whore who only exposes her bottom to a young Ganymede, will make him discharge almost to blood, while the same action shall produce but an ordinary sensation in another. The jerks and heaves of a strong lustful woman will plunge the man of vivid temperament into a torrent of delight, while they would be death to the effeminate strokes of the decrepid old lecher.

Q.—What are the characteristics by which you discover a whore from another woman?

A.—Her dress is gay and flaunting—her manners loose and unreserved, her looks bold and lascivious—and her conversation voluptuous and enticing. By these means her trade is known. Were she to affect modesty, there are many men so timid and bashful they would be afraid to accost her, and she would lose much good practice by assuming a decorous demeanour which might be misunderstood.

Q.—But is it not possible for a whore to imitate the decency and reserve of a modest woman?

A.—Yes; and those of this class are most subtle. They allure by that means the simpletons they wish to dupe. They affect to be greatly enraged at their propositions, in order to entrap them the more securely: and how many are there caught in this snare who flatter themselves they have got something choice and safe, until they find themselves well poxed. Some whores make great profits by this kind of commerce, but it is only those who can move in a respectable style that can conveniently act this hypocritical part.

Q.—Have all women a decided penchant to become whores?

A.—Yes; all are, or desire to be whores, and it is nothing but pride or fear that restrains the greater part, and every girl who yields for the first time, is from that moment a decided whore. The smock once lifted, she is as familiarized to the game as if she had played it for ten years.

Q.—Ought a whore to give herself up to the pleasure whenever she submits in the embraces of a man?

A.—There is a medium in everything. It would be very imprudent in a whore to indulge herself in stroking to excess, as it would soon make the flesh soft and flabby; but there is a refinement in pleasure, which an accomplished whore should know how to use. A word, a gesture, a touch at the critical moment, produces in men the illusion of pleasure; and as the heart is an impenetrable abyss, the crafty courtesan often fulfils, by a fictitious enjoyment, the luxurious views of the men who content themselves with the appearance.

Q.—Ought a whore to administer as much pleasure to the man who only gives her a crown as to him who pays her liberally?

A.—It is certain that a whore ought to live by her vocation. The great art of a courtezan who would acquire a reputation, is to avoid appearing mercenary. She must study her men, and with some refuse the proffered fee. She will meet with those who will be susceptible of this delicacy, and be touched by the apparent disinterestedness shown them, imagining that she is more taken with their person than their money. The pleasure which does not appear to them to be bought, is more piquant and more thought of; and a whore is often a great gainer by this kind of artifice.

Q.—How ought a whore to conduct herself when her charms have attracted a customer?

A.—She must make him feel himself perfectly at home. The first thing a man does, when entering the lodgings of a girl, is to explore her bubbies, then her buttcks, and next her 'bush'. While he is doing this, she ought to unbutton his breeches. Now is the time to use endearing expressions and exciting titillations, and now is also the proper period for demanding her fee, which will be the more readily given to prevent delay between the preludes and the moment of enjoyment. It will not be amiss to mention in this place the rapacious custom of many courtezans. If a gentleman offers them a crown, they will demand two. If he yields, their importunity increases, they want a ribbon or a ring, in short, they are never satisfied. This conduct, however, is very injurious to them, because the men's minds being intent on pleasure, are greatly disgusted by being so long baulked through the avarice of the women.

Q.—What are the attributes and utensils requisite for the chamber of a woman of pleasure?

A.—She ought to have some good rods hung up in sight; also in her drawers she ought to have scourges of different kinds of leather, a cat-of-ninetails made of knotted whip cord, and one with pins fastened to the thongs, together with straps, bandages, and cords, strong enough to bind a powerful man.

Q.—What are the uses of all these things?

A.—They are of very great importance in the profession of a courtezan, because many men would never visit her if she did not keep rods and know how to use them. Flagellation is one of the most powerful excitements that can be resorted to when friction and coaxing have not been able to procure an erection. Give a man twenty or thirty hard cuts on the backside with a good rod, and it will soon rouse his energies, and make him fit for action. The passion for birch discipline is not confined to persons advanced in life, you will meet with candidates for it of all ages, from eighteen to eighty. Some will only require it gently, whilst others will not be satisfied unless you wear out two rods upon them, and cause the blood to run down at their heels. They generally like to be strapped down to a couch or horse, or to have their hands tied firmly to a bed post Courtezans in good practice have curious machines made on purpose to confine the votories of discipline hand and foot while they receive the torture. Some copulate immediately afterward; others like to be horsed on the back of an athletic female and discharged through the friction against her back. You will find this class of customers have more odd whims, strange fancies, and fantastical caprices than any others. Some will require to be flogged in woman's clothes; and before they undergo the operation, will call in the aid of a great variety of preludes and ceremonies, without which their imagination will not be sufficiently worked upon.

Q.—Ought a courtezan to demand a double fee for the execution of so fatiguing an operation?

A.—Certainly; for although she may derive a degree of pleasure in flogging a handsome backside, and may sometimes even 'spend' whilst engaged in a flagellation, yet there are *paillards*, who would tire out the arm of the most vigorous woman who might herself have a passion for this kind of excitement. She ought, therefore, to be well paid for the rods she uses in this tragic-comic ceremony.

Q.—What language ought a courtezan to use during a flagellation?

A.—Her conversation ought to be suited to the character and humour of the *paillard* whom she fustigates. Some like to be sworn at and assailed with the most violent and blackguard terms of abuse while their flesh is being cut to pieces. Others again, whose passions and humours are more mild, are desirous that you should renew with them the innocent sports of childhood, and pretend to administer juvenile corrections, calling them naughty boys, little scoundrels, mischievous rogues, dunces, ordering them to put down their breeches, and threatening to whip them until the blood comes. These, and many other phrases of a similar nature, which a skilful courtezan knows how to use, have a wonderful effect in procuring an erection and making them discharge.

Q.—Can you give me any other information relative to this strange lech?

A.—Some men instead of being whipped themselves by a female, have a desire to be the operator. Their lech is to flog a girl who has a fine plump bottom. They like to have her hands tied to a sofa or horse, but generally prefer having her legs left at liberty, as her kicking, wriggling and plunging, adds much to their amusement. The quivering and reddening of her buttocks under the rod, is to them a powerful source of excitement. There are, in all establishments devoted to venereal pleasures, women trained on purpose to receive severe whippings, many of whom make fortunes entirely by the hardness of their posteriors. There is also a third class of *paillards* connected with this singular lech, who neither wish to whip nor be whipped, but are satisfied with the sight of it.

Q.—What other attributes and utensils should adorn the chamber of a *fille de joie?*

A.—She ought to have a collection of lascivious pictures and bawdy books, illustrated with prints, some *baudruches* and two or three dildoes.

Q.—What am I to understand by *baudruches?*

A.—They are little bags or sheaths made from the blind gut of the lamb, with which a man envelopes his pego when he strokes a woman of whom he is not sure. By this means he is protected against the pox; but the precaution, though prudent, is often displeasing to women of a lustful temperament, as it deprives them of the boiling injection. They are also used to prevent getting modest women with child, and are of great importance to married women whose husbands are abroad.

Q.—What do you mean by 'dildoes'?

A.—A dildoe is intended originally for the use of those who could not get the real thing. It is of very great antiquity, being well known to the ancient Hebrews, Chaldeans, Persians, &c. The Egyptians made them of porcelain; the Greeks of wood and ivory; the Roman ladies preferred them of glass, and called them 'Phalli'. We, however, make them of india-rubber, and cause them to perform as well, if not better than the real thing. They are much used by nuns in convents, and by widows and old maids; but the use a courtezan has for them is only to gratify the caprices of her visitors.

Q.—To what age can a courtezan exercise her profession with honour and profit?

A.—That depends a great deal on temperament. The fair women ought to quit this trade before the dark ones, as their flesh is more subject to become flabby. A woman who has been in the seraglios until she is forty, must be very much the worse for wear, and will find it prudent to retire.

Q.—What then must a courtezan do who has grown old in the combats of Venus, without having laid anything by to support her declining years?

A.—That fault, which is almost universal with women of pleasure, is not then to be remedied. Plutus generally flies from the boudoirs which are deserted by love; and an old whore has no alternative but to be either a bawd or servant to another whore; for no longer able to make dupes, she must content herself with holding the candle, and being sometimes the patient spectatress of certain pleasures, the remembrance of which must cause the most painful regrets. Her only hope can be the chance of occasionally cajoling a gouty old codger, or a young fellow rendered stupid through drunkenness. The courtezan on the contrary, who, during the prosperity of youth, has laid by a competence, shall still have as much sensual pleasure as she can wish, even under wrinkles, and old age, for her money will procure her as many strokers as she pleases. She may often in the embraces of a robust operator forget her decrepitude and enjoy the pleasure of youth over again; for a woman can never be too old to receive delight, if rogered by a vigorous young man: while life is in her body she is capable of enjoyment. Therefore if she has money, she may be stroked till the day of her death; and what death can be more sweet than that of a whore who dies while she is spending?

The New Ladies' Tickler

he New Ladies' Tickler; or
The Adventures of Lady Lovesport and The Audacious Harry
appeared from the notorious publisher of pornography, William
Dugdale, in 1866 with what Ashbee described as 'eight badly done
lithographs from designs by Edward Sellon'. Dugdale catalogued it
at two guineas. The edition before me, in its original green wrap-
pers, is dated 1890; it is the sort of comparatively well-written
melange of flagellation, sex and general sportive 'naughtiness'—told
in the form of eight letters—that would have undoubtedly ensured
its revival on several occasions. Ashbee evidently rated it high in its
genre, for although he accorded it a short notice he noted it as a
'well-written book . . . very voluptuous': a comparatively rare accolade
from this benign, cautious and ever-accurate authority.

LETTER I

EMILY TO LUCY

I think you would pity me if you could see the sad state to which I am reduced, and the shifts I am obliged to have recourse to, in order to appease the desires so natural to our age. How I long to be back again with you at school, that we might again enjoy our usual sweet intercourse together, and indulge in all those frolics and pastimes which, ever since our acquaintance commenced, have given me, and I am sure you also, so much delight.

Here, though I have returned to the scenes of my youth, everything seems new and strange. There is no one to whom I can talk confidentially, and confide all my little woes and wants. My aunt, though kind, is reserved with me, and Harry—the meeting with whom I anticipated would afford me so much delight—is not here, and I cannot find that there is any prospect of my even seeing him at present.

I do so wish we were again in our snug little petticoats apartment at Miss Birch's, for though the lessons were tedious and tiresome, and our worthy school-mistress's castigation was sometimes more severe than was quite agreeable to our poor little bottoms, still even that was not all pain, and how well we used to make up for it, when we were safely established for the night in our own little beds, and alternately crept from one to the other, in order to enjoy all those delicious pleasures which you first taught me, and which we used to carry to the utmost extent that our heated imaginations could possibly invent, to ensure our luscious enjoyment.

But as I have no adventures to write to you about at present, and very little prospect of any, I think I cannot do better than redeem my promise of giving you some details of our proceedings here before I joined you at school, and which gave rise to the anticipation I expressed to you of having something agreeable to communicate to you during my residence here, but which, alas, I am sorry to find, has not been realized.

You are aware that I have been brought up by my aunt, Lady Lovesport, with whom I lived till, at the age of ten, I was sent to school. As you have seen Lady Lovesport, and know well what an extremely handsome fine looking woman she is, I need not describe her to you, more especially as I shall have occasion afterwards to say

K

something regarding her person. You are, however, perhaps not aware that she was married, when very young, to a rich old man, with whom she led but an unhappy life, though, by-the-bye, her husband somewhat made up for this, by leaving her nearly all his fortune, coupled with the condition that she was not to marry again, under the penalty of losing it. On his death she made up her mind not to throw away her wealth, nor subject her person to the control of another husband, and she has ever since remained in a state of single blessedness. As her income is large, she lives in very good style, and has every opportunity of indulging in any fancy she may take, and I have reason to believe that she does not hesitate to seek for amusement wherever she thinks she is likely to find it.

My earliest years passed very pleasantly. My aunt was always kind to me, and though I was kept strictly to my lessons, still, as long as I was attentive and diligent, every indulgence was shown to me. But if, on any occasion, I failed in doing what was required of me, my poor bottom was pretty sure to smart for it. My aunt always undertook the duty of correcting me herself, and when punishment was to be inflicted, I was taken to a small room adjoining her bedroom, where I was placed across her knees, my petticoats were taken up, and a birch rod applied pretty smartly to my naked posteriors.

On these occasions I generally struggled a good deal. I soon fancied that, by tossing myself about, and pretending to suffer more than I really did, my aunt's heart was softened, and consequently the stripes inflicted upon me were of a less severe nature than when I lay like a log on her knees, and shewed no symptoms of feeling the pain. However this may be, it usually happened that between my struggles and her endeavours to retain me on her knee, her clothes would also be tossed up, and before the conclusion of my punishment, her thighs were generally as bare as my own, and I lay with my naked belly and thighs pressed against her naked person. On these occasions I could not but admire the softness and beauty of the charms which were thus exposed to me, and to wonder at the profusion of beautiful curly hair, which adorned the secret spot often presented to my sight, so different from the bare unfledged gap, which was beginning to attract my own curiosity.

Nor were my opportunities for viewing her lovely person confined to the exhibition thus made during my punishment. Lady Lovesport's residence is, you are aware, on the seacoast. Within a short distance of the house there is a retired bay, shut in by two projecting rocks on either side, so as not to be approached, except through our own grounds. Here a small bathing house had been erected, and we were accustomed to repair thither every day in fine weather. During the warm summer months we used often to wander there by ourselves, without any attendant. Generally we were in the habit of wearing bathing gowns, but it would sometimes happen that, after sporting and toying together for a while, Lady Lovesport would either get angry, or at least pretend to do so, at something or another I did, and would hastily tear a few twigs from the young birch trees which grew on the shore, and making me take off my bathing gown, she would apply the rod to my posteriors. But on these occasions this was always done sportively, and evidently without any intention of inflicting pain. Nay, she would even sometimes strip off her own wet attire, which interfered with her movements, and arming herself with one rod, and allowing me to provide myself with another, we would chase each other in the water or up and down the soft sands, and when one succeeded in catching the other, there always followed a smart application of the soft green twigs to the buttocks and thighs of the fugitive.

After this sport had been repeated several times, I began to observe that my aunt always selected one spot for this amusement, exactly in front of a dense thicket, which rather projected out from the rest of the shore, and a boundary was fixed on each side, beyond which it was declared we were not to go, so that in chasing each other, we had always to pass close in front of this thicket. On one occasion I was a little startled by observing, as I thought, a slight movement in the thicket, as if someone was passing through the bushes, but my aunt laughed at me, said it was only a rabbit hopping about, and at the same time applied her rod so vigorously to my posteriors that she soon gave me something else to think about. I was, however, induced, after this, to keep a watch upon the thicket, and occasionally I was convinced I saw a similar movement. Nay, once I was pretty certain that I caught a glimpse of a face, which seemed to me in the slight glance I had of it, to be very like that of a young gentleman who resided in the neighbourhood, whose family was very intimate with my aunt, and who himself was a frequent visitor at our house. But as I had no wish for a repetition of the severe discipline which my first observation had brought upon me, I said no more about it. It also struck me as somewhat singular

147

that when we returned to the house after any of these frolicsome pastimes, we were quite certain either to find the young gentleman there, or he would arrive very soon after us.

But I think I have made this letter long enough—so adieu for the present.

Emily

LETTER II
EMILY TO LUCY

Not having any news to give you, for everything here is as dull and uninteresting as ever, I shall resume my story.

A young lady, the daughter of a friend of my aunt, had been on a visit to us for some time. She was an extremely beautiful girl, about fifteen years of age, with one of the handsomest and most elegantly shaped figures I had ever seen. For some reason, for which I could not well account, my aunt seemed to have taken a dislike to her, and was continually finding fault with her. It is true that Maria gave her considerable cause for dissatisfaction, for she was idle and lazy, constantly getting into mischief, and doing something or other which she knew quite well would displease my aunt, Lady Lovesport had very often threatened to whip her unless she behaved herself better. Maria seemed to pay no attention to what she said, but I, who knew my aunt better, had little doubt that she would carry her threat into execution.

One forenoon we were sitting together at our work. My aunt had that morning been very much displeased with Maria for some mischief she had committed, and she told her that before she went out she intended to punish her for it with a sound flogging. I was seated with my face to the window, which commanded a view of the avenue, and I saw Mr. Everard, the young gentleman to whom I have already alluded, coming towards the house. I was a little surprised that no announcement was made to us of his arrival. In a short time, however my aunt's confidential servant came into the room, and whispered a few words in her ear. Soon afterwards my aunt rose up and giving me some work to do, which would occupy me some time, she told me to make myself ready to accompany her on a visit she was going to make in an hour afterwards. She then desired Maria to follow her to her apartment.

I was very certain that my aunt's purpose was to punish the girl, and I could not help somehow connecting this punishment with the arrival of Mr. Everard. I felt a strong desire to ascertain whether I was right in this conjecture. The idea took such a strong hold upon my mind, that I determined to be a spectatress of the punishment, and knowing a back way to a closet which would give me a full view of all my aunt's doings in her own room, you may guess I soon dropped the work I had to do, and hied to my place of espionage, finding myself not a moment too soon, for she had already got the trembling Maria divested of everything but her chemise, and I could see that her bubbies were sufficiently grown to swell out, and show their charming rotundity in the most enticing manner possible. As soon as she was thus stripped, my aunt made her place her arms behind her, and tied them with a handkerchief behind her back. She then took another handkerchief, and fastened it firmly over her eyes, so as to blindfold her completely.

In this condition she led her to a couch, which, fortunately, was in full view from my hiding place, and made her lie down upon it, at the same time lifting up her chemise, and fastening it around her waist, so as to leave all her person below that perfectly naked. Indeed, from the loose manner in which that garment hung around her, my aunt easily contrived to lay bare the whole of the upper part of her person likewise, the chemise merely forming a sort of girdle round her waist, where it was retained by the manner in which her arms were bound.

When all this was arranged, my aunt made a signal to someone in the bedroom, and, to my great surprise, though I must say, I had rather anticipated something of the sort, I saw Mr. Everard steal gently from the one room to the other, and place himself at the back of the couch, leaning his arms upon it, and gazing intently, though, of course, in perfect silence, upon the lovely form thus exposed, naked, before his eyes. He had taken off his coat and waistcoat, and his boots, but otherwise he was completely dressed.

No sooner had he taken his place than my aunt began to apply the rod to the exquisite posteriors which were thus presented to her in such an inviting position for the birch. She was not very severe at first, and Maria lay pretty still, though her shrinking, quivering flesh shewed that she felt keenly the stinging touches. As the charming

Wicked Victorians

buttocks began to be reddened by this exhilarating exercise, my aunt seemed to get excited and heaten with her work, and plied the rod more sharply and vigorously.

In proportion, as she felt the pain increase, Maria began to exhibit symptoms of the intensity of her feelings, she turned and twisted about, and writhed her body in every manner of strange contortion, sometimes raising up her buttocks by resting on her knees, so as to exhibit her lovely belly, sometimes trying to avoid the sharp stripes by turning herself round to my side, thereby giving me a full view of the front part of her person, with the lovely characteristic which distinguishes our sex, shewing its delicious lips opening and closing again, as they were affected by the nature of her contortions, and the constant twisting and writhing of her body.

When this took place my aunt was pretty sure, by a sharp application of the rod, to make her turn round again, but when, on the other hand, she moved herself so as to expose the same delightful sight to the evidently charmed gaze of Mr. Everard, she rather suspended her blows, or merely applied them so lightly as to induce Maria to remain for a time in the same attitude.

During the operation my aunt's robe flew open, and I discovered that she had nothing on beneath it, except a thin chemise. Her robe hanging down over her shoulders, exhibited her entire bosom, naked, with its charming promontories, which, though more full grown, and considerably larger and more mature in their proportions, were equally lovely in shape and colour. Occasionally, as she changed her position, I could catch a glimpse of her naked legs and thighs, though these were more generally turned in the opposite direction from me.

At length, as if exhausted with the exertion, and tired of standing longer, she sat down on the couch, and as Maria's motions were now becoming more fierce and energetic, she placed her arm round the girl's waist, as if to restrain her struggles, though it rather appeared to me as if it was done with the view of procuring a better exhibition of every part of her person. At the same time my aunt stretched out her own legs at full length before her, opening her thighs a little apart, and allowing her robe to fall on each side, so as to disclose them to view.

As soon as Mr. Everard perceived this, he gently stole round, and got on his knees beside her, and spreading her legs still further apart, he raised up her chemise, and disclosed the centre of pleasure.

I had often in our bathing expeditions, seen and admired the lovely spot, but I had never before beheld it in the same state of excitement. It glowed and quivered under his warm and exciting touches, while the strange motions she made with her legs and buttocks amused and surprised me.

She still continued to apply the birch to poor Maria's posteriors, and to feast her own and Mr. Everard's eyes with the exquisite beauties that were developed before them in every possible attitude and position that could excite the senses.

In the course of a minute or two, she made a sign to Mr. Everard, who immediately rose, and retreated to the bedroom as silently as he had entered. After adjusting her robe she now announced to the weeping Maria that her punishment was at an end; took off the bandage, unloosened her hands and told her to dress herself, and retire to her own room.

As soon as Maria had departed, my aunt repaired to the bedroom, I remained on the watch for some time, in the hope of seeing her and Mr. Everard return to the boudoir, but, though I could hear them talking in the bedroom, they did not come back. As the bedroom had another door, by which she might go out without my hearing her, I was obliged to make good my retreat, for fear of being caught, but it was nearly an hour afterwards before my aunt sent for me to go out with her.

I managed to obtain a sight of two or three scenes of a similar kind, which generally terminated pretty much in the same manner, so it is needless to describe them. But I must give you the particulars of the last one, in which my dear Harry was the victim. This however, must be reserved for another opportunity.

Ever your's,
Emily

Eveline

U NNOTICED by a majority
of too-hasty 'historians' of erotica, *Eveline* represents one of the very
rare examples of a pornographic novel that has actually been 'improved and extended' by someone other than the original author.

Ashbee noted the original work in two volumes as having been
published c. 1843. 'At the beginning,' he observed, 'the book is
fairly well written but towards the end it becomes tame, same and
fragmentary'. Some years after Ashbee's bibliography appeared,
there was published a three-volume edition of *Eveline* with a fore-
word by its anonymous editor in which he remarks that 'being
struck with the unusual quality of the original, I undertook to supply
as nearly as possible the numerous omissions marked by half pages
of asterisks throughout the book, following what I conceived to be
the intention of the author to make his story a succinct narration ...
I have followed closely throughout the style of the original composition, and now present this revised edition of a very singular old work
to the curious in such literature'.

I know of only two other instances in which a *lengthening* and
'improvement' of an erotic novel has occurred and these in an
American paperback edition of *The Autobiography of a Flea* (c. 1887)
which Pendulum books first published in a two volume translation
and of which they then commissioned a two-volume sequel (c. 1968).

These volumes, respectively of 240pp and 256pp., are constructed with such remarkable sustained skill in sequential faithfulness to the manner and style of the original work that they would be likely to deceive bibliographers of many decades hence if their provenance were not otherwise known. Yet a fourth volume of continuation has also appeared (1969) which is clearly by a different and wholly indifferent writer who has paid no attention whatever to the skills of his immediate predecessor. The fourth volume in fact bears no relation whatever in plot, characters or setting to the preceding ones.

A second example of elongation is an extension of *The Way of a Man with a Maid,* from Taurus Press, U.S.A. (1969), which faithfully copies the style of the original and retains the principal characters. In essence, however, the story is wholly repetitive of the first half of the Victorian original whereas the first two 'new' volumes to *The Autobiography of a Flea* are inventive of plot.

How much the editor of *Eveline* added to produce *A Modern Eveline* cannot be judged in the absence of the original, since the British Museum have lost possession of the early edition which he noted as being in the Private Case collection. Certainly there are no visible seams.

Eveline is a one-girl sex gang, one who plots her sensual indulgences with all the skill of a football pool permutation. Read in toto, she is undoubtedly the most artless, observant and coherent of all the fictional creatures of her genre not excluding *Fanny Hill.*

CHAPTER ONE

I am considered by those of my acquaintance to be a pattern of propriety. I am pointed out by envious mothers as an excellent example of careful training, combined with the advantages of a Continental finishing course at a most select *Pensionnat de Demoiselles* in the environs of Paris. I am the invited of very strict old maids because I affect to enter into their schemes for the conversion of innumerable savages, am liberal of purse and reticent of tongue. The latter quality runs in my family. Our history demands an extraordinary amount of it. It is quite as well that it should have been so treated. There are at least two families of high and ancient aristocratic pretensions whose loud-tongued, gambling, drinking, male descendants openly boast that they have never allowed a maiden of their noble line to pass, as a maiden, out of the family into the arms of her spouse. Ours is a third; only we are not so simple as to publish the fact.

I am not by any means a saint. In my appearance and outward habits I am not so straightlaced as I am represented. I do not set up for particular formality in my daily pursuits. I am only quiet, observing, always affable and sometimes a trifle volatile. The men call me dull and say, 'A pretty girl but you know, dear boy, there is no fun in her. No use to try it on, dear old chappie, you'll come off second best'.

'Fun,' in the mind of the society man of the present day, means immorality. They adopt the word because it is a light and gay style of describing the loose conditions which bind together all that they care for in the nature of modern society. At present, society is content to parade itself with a superficial and very flimsy disguise. In a few years, at its present rate of progress, it will walk barefaced in the open light of day.

I am not going to moralize; I do not even wish to be a self-appointed censor of the times in which I live. I do not personally care a pin what becomes of society, so long as I succeed in avoiding the arrows of detraction, scorn and contempt which it launches against any member luckless enough to be exposed to it. I can say that I hardly think it will do so in my case; at any rate I will take all possible precautions to pursue my silent path of sensual indulgence in obscurity and peace.

My father, Sir Edward L——, Baronet, started life as a rich man, rich even in the days of treble millionaires, American heiresses and other innovations too numerous to mention. He entered the army, served with his regiment in India, and returning to that Empire after a short furlough, met and married a nobody with whom he was shut up for a month or more on his voyage out. She was good-looking, tall and coarse. He soon tired of her. After dragging her about for three months with his regiment, he sent her home to England. I do not know that I inherit any single trait of my mother's personality, and I rejoice to think so. She never cared for me or took any particular notice of me. I had two brothers older than myself. Of the elder I may speak later; I knew little of him in my childhood. As for Percy, we were companions until I was sent to school and he to Rugby. He was 15 and I 13 when these important events happened.

I suppose I was always curious and inquiring as a child. I have been told so. Personally, I only remember a few prominent incidents of my early childhood. It was not a joyous or even happy one. My brother and I were thrown much together. He was curious also. Together we secretly investigated the remarkable differences in our physiological structures. We came to the natural conclusion that such opposite developments must have been designed for some purpose which we did not understand. The tree of knowledge was being denied us, so we set about making our own discoveries. The result was that we found a certain indefinite gratification when, being at either end of a large marble bath, our toes encountered certain exposed portions of each other's person which at all other times we were told we must hide and never talk about. Secretly, also, we mutually inspected these remarkably different developments; it was a new field of investigation and we enjoyed it. We pursued our studies at such intervals as our privacy and our opportunities permitted. We slept in the same room and we would steal furtively into each other's bed to whisper and wonder at the delight which the feeling and caressing of these dissimilarities afforded us. In short, we masturbated each other until my brother Percy, at the age of 15, attained a precocious development of his private organs, quite sufficient to destroy all vestige of maidenhood in his younger sister, two years his junior.

At this age we were separated, as I have already related. A couple of years at a Brighton seminary, exclusively for the 'daughters of gentlemen,' did not eradicate the lessons in physiology I had already learned. Quite the contrary: I listened while my companions compared notes, and I found that most of the girls were equally well informed. Indeed, one or two of the elder 'daughters of gentlemen' told us of the junior classes, while we listened to the absorbing topic with rapt attention, what a naked man was like with curly hair on his belly, and a thing dangling between his legs which they described as being twice the size of my brother Percy's. They went further, and one averred that she had seen and handled one. That they grew stiff and stood upright. In that condition men endeavoured to thrust them into girls.

I listened and said nothing, and for my silence they called me a little fool and innocent. Even at that early period of my existence

I had imbibed the instinct of reticence, so generally absent in young women.

Two years of study of all the conventional and impractical subjects to which the 'daughters of gentlemen' are subjected afforded me ample opportunities for acquiring the rudiments of a society education. How much longer I might have remained at the Brighton seminary I know not, but an untoward accident put an end to my career there, as also the 'Select Establishment' itself.

It happened thus. Among the domestics was a page, who had commenced his duties there as a small boy. As he was very quiet and well conducted, he remained a long time, in fact grew to puberty in that house. Nobody seemed to notice the change. The lad waited at table in gorgeous buttons and claret-coloured cloth, did other useful duties and was quite unrestricted about the premises. One of the elder girls, however, whose inquisitive genius had discovered the interesting fact that he had hair on his belly and a thing which stood upright, essayed to take advantage of this development. She induced him to put it into her on more than one occasion, with the result that she was discovered to be enceinte. The fact could not be concealed; the Brighton press took it up and the 'Select Establishment' was closed forever.

My father was at this time on military service in India. Through influence, although a comparatively young man, he had risen to the command of his regiment. I was not allowed to remain at home. My prayer for a governess was peremptorily refused. My mother could not endure my presence. I was packed off to a *Pensionnat de Demoiselles* near Paris, one which had been specially recommended by the Lady-mother of the promising and 'honourable' young members of a noble house.

It was at this place that I was destined to be initiated into the more practical knowledge of mankind in so far as his sexual instincts and aptitudes are concerned. The house was large and stood in its own grounds with a short garden in front leading to the *Loge de Concierge,* and the great iron gates which closed the establishment to the public road. The lodge was tenanted by a singular individual, a hunchback who had held the office of janitor for some years. He was a man of some 45 years and stood about four feet and some inches in his boots. His hump was a sufficient disfigurement, but his ugliness, his long hair and his huge hands and feet, added greatly to his weird appearance. With all this, however, his face was considered a perfectly harmless one, not repulsive, and his manner the reverse of the brutal. He was considered a perfectly harmless unfortunate, bore an excellent character, and had the entire confidence of Madame St. C——, proprietress and directress of the *Pensionnat*.

When I became intimate with my fellow pupils I learned that they were quite as well acquainted with natural phenomena as my old friends at Brighton: indeed, more than one of the French girls made no scruple of boasting of her exploits. One in particular spoke openly of her acquaintance with a certain playfellow of the opposite sex who had obtained from her such favours as only lovers are permitted.

The concierge was allowed to eke out his small revenue by the harmless privilege of retailing sweets, chocolate, etc., to the *pensionnaires*. The girls, during the hours of recreation, would return from his little den in the lodge with red cheeks and with their mouths full of sugarplums. I never had the childs' weakness for bon-bons. I was not fond of them. The concierge and myself remained strangers for a considerable time after my arrival. I often noticed the man took extra trouble to salute me in passing. He offered such civilities as were decorous and polite. The girls spoke sometimes of little commissions which they had given him to perform for them. I soon found that he was considered a safe intermediary between the world at large and the elder girls.

When I crossed from Dover to Calais en route to Paris, in the charge of a governess who collected English pupils, I chanced to sit next to two gentlemen who conversed together of Voltaire and his works. I possessed a girl's natural curiosity—I listened. They mentioned his allusions to Charlemagne. One exclaimed how he recognized the biting sarcasm of the style. He quoted the account of the great king's private vices. The other cited Addison to show how little regard the great Frenchman had for virtue in itself. It was an interesting dispute. They raised their voices, I made notes and determined to read Voltaire and judge for myself. I did not want bonbons; I wanted Voltaire.

* * * * *

I am dearly fond of the beautiful in art. What can be the difference between the beautiful in a mirror and the beauty in a picture? Rely upon it, every woman is certain to know the exact measure of her good looks, if she possesses any. She is sure to be reminded of her correct appreciation of her charms. She may think she can impose on others by her beauty. It is only by the flattery of the honest opinions she obtains that her vanity is touched, that comparisons are made. When she goes home and sees herself in privacy, she knows the naked truth for better or for worse.

When a man tells me he thinks me the most beautiful girl in the world, I know he is talking nonsense. When he simply and obviously admires me for my comeliness, I may believe him. If he goes further, if he ventures to speak of love to me, I know I have excited his desire. I can see it in his eyes. It is evident in the parted lips, the ardent, furtive glances with which I feel he is striving to pierce the veils in which modesty—save the mark!—robes the nude form of woman. He is forming his ideas on the subject of my nudity—of the extent of my fabricated personality. Poor man, if he could only look in reality, below, he would find there was something there—Nature unadorned. In fancy, he gives his ideal full freedom. He sees me as his lust would have me. He sees the perfect bust, the waist, the ample buttocks which no dressmaker ever pads with wretched cotton wool. In fancy he beholds me stripped—at his mercy—though small mercy I should receive at his hands. He rages in private. He snorts like a stallion over a young mare. I have no contempt for this poor creature. Shall I confess the truth? I feel intensely for him.

That confession does not prevent me from displaying to him such attractions as my beauty and knowledge enable me to excite him with. His agony of lust is to me a selfish gratification. It is joy to me to watch his hardly concealed emotion. I know him. I treat him simply as he would treat me. I am, in his short-sighted view, too innocent and too young, altogether too inexperienced, to understand anything connected with the realities of sensual instincts. His lust extends to my flesh; in his licentiousness he pictures to himself all the delights he would enjoy in my possession. In my innocent young charms.

Could the man who struts in society only know how his glances at Eveline are noted and enjoyed, he might indeed be more bold, but he would nonetheless meet with the failure he merits. She is not the girl, young and innocent as he deems her, to play the puppet while he pulls the strings and boasts loud-tongued to his club of his society successes.

* * * * *

A fine morning. Actual sunlight, and in London! I sprang out of bed just at eight o'clock. My cold tub is there ready. How refreshing it is! How I glow, all fresh and red as I stand and rub myself down. The act reminds me of Jim—of grooming a horse. I should like Jim to groom me now. Well, should I, really? Yes—that I should. Then I remember the sight which for a moment met my gaze through the stable windows. I commence my morning toilet. I gradually mature at the same time an idea which more and more becomes fixed in my mind. My passions I fear are not always made subservient to my higher perceptions. It is my nature to give them flight at times. To indulge them against my cooler nature. How can I, with my temperament, stop to think of risks or results? So my fancy can run free now. In fancy I am again at the stable window. That does not prevent me from completing my morning toilet. I descend to breakfast. Papa is there already, his newspapers and letters before him.

'Good morning, Eveline. Here is a letter which will interest you'.

A large envelope enclosing a card. The arms of the Duke of M——. The invitation at last to the costume ball!

'It will be magnificent, my darling. You will make a sensation. All the guests are to represent some particular personality. How will you go? You would be adorable as Anne Boleyn'.

And my papa would look defiantly inscrutable as Charlemagne.

'Oh, Papa! It is fixed. You must go as Charlemagne!'

'And you, Eveline?'

'I shall represent my great grandmother, Papa. I have ordered all. We have her jewels. We have in the great wardrobe the dresses she wore at my age. You told me yourself how alike I was to her in the picture in your study. I can imitate the pose, the look, everything. It is fixed, Papa—you will not deny your own little girl?'

He never denied me anything. He would go to the Duchess' ball as Charlemagne, if practicable. I, as my own great grandmother.

'Do not forget we dine tonight at Lady Lesselton's. There will be some nice people there who are always worth meeting. She is very erratic in her assemblage of guests at these little dinners. You may depend on it, you have been asked to meet someone in particular; very young ladies are not always selected for these affairs'.

'I will not forget. I shall try to look as bright as possible to please my dear Papa first, and the somebody in particular next'.

'Naughty girl! Kiss me!'

The dinner passed pleasantly enough. Lady Lesselton laid herself out to be very nice to me. I was coupled with a very delightful old man—the magistrate of Bow Street. Sir Langham Beamer was a bachelor, a gentleman and a man of taste. I like old people. I took particular pains to be agreeable to him. He was a very smart and gay old gentleman from the old school. He loved the company of the young. He was evidently delighted to find his hostess had not forgotten his foible. I heard him express his gratification in no measured language to her after dinner. I found him full of anecdotes and information with a distinct tendency to revert in conversation to his profession. I thought him charming. He made me promise to come around with Papa and see him administer his functions in his Police Court.

At quite an early hour we returned home. It was the brougham they sent for us. Sir Langham Beamer put me in himself. Papa received me in his arms. We rolled away, our lips sealed together, our hearts beating on each other, our hands—ah me!—our hands ... The restraint was dreadful, the longing terrible. Between the two I was nearly mad. Papa, I could see, was not much better.

* * * * *

'Covent Garden—Opera—oh! Here it is. *Faust* tonight. Look, what a splendid cast! Will you go, Eveline? The music of Gounod always delights you. Will you go?'

'Yes, dear Papa. It will cheer me up. I feel I want to hear something sympathetic. I love Gounod and I am not tired of *Faust*.'

'Agreed then; we will order the dinner and the carriage in good time'.

For some days he had withdrawn himself from my company a good deal. Only on such occasions as were unavoidably necessary did he come to me, or venture himself within range of my influence. I was certain he had been forming resolutions to restrain his passion.

My sensations as I prepared myself for the evening were the wildest anticipations. On this occasion I determined to go through with my intrigue. I was infatuated. I had nursed this passion a long time. I had built up all the most captivating and extraordinary theories respecting it. I imagined the pleasure, the sensuous gratification to be derived from it, as supreme. The lines of Voltaire haunted me. We had already gone too far to turn back. He knew it as well as I did. It was thus that I dressed myself to please him. I decked myself out in just that dainty and coquettish style which I was sure would swell his lust. The corsage just showed enough to make the observer wish to see more. My whole toilet was of the ephemeral character which would serve only to heighten the unruly passion which burned to fever heat in his veins. I was armed. I had no regrets. I only dreaded failure.

The great theatre was crowded. The atmosphere was oppressive. Sir Edward leaned over the back of my chair.

'My darling Eveline, you look more beautiful than ever tonight'.

'I am always glad to please my dear Papa'.

'Your dress is perfection; it leaves nothing to be desired'.

'Absolutely nothing, Papa'.

'Why do you say that, my dear child?'

I took his hand and held it. I leaned back in my seat and put my face close to his. His eyes shot flames of passion. I half shut mine and sighed. He kissed the nape of my neck just under my hair. I squeezed his hand, and patted it with my softly gloved fingers. I put my right hand on his mouth. His breath came fast. I trembled.

'My beautiful—my darling!'

We heard the last beautiful serenade. It was the *entr'acte*. His arm was around my waist, my hand wandered slowly and caressingly upon his left thigh.

We were well behind the curtain and in the recess of the box. I threw my head back. He kissed me on the lips, a long, lingering embrace which spoke volumes of his desire.

'Shall we go to the restaurant and sup there again, my sweet?'

'Yes, papa. It is most oppressive here tonight'.

The supper was exquisite. The wine warmed our blood. Sir Edward drank freely. I read a fixed purpose in his eyes. He could not keep his hands off me. He helped me to all the choicest morsels. By his desire I retained my gloves. He watched the exit of the waiter and tipped him handsomely. Then he locked the door.

L

The Romance of Lust

ITH the publication of this incredible book in four volumes, between 1873 and 1876, the pornographic novel reached its apogee. What was incredible about it was not its subject matter, for it had all been done before, but its length —the fact that any one man could have sustained this interminable story of incest and extra-familial sex without boring himself into the grave before its 611 printed pages were completed.

The Romance of Lust was, according to Ashbee, 'not the produce of a single pen, but consists of several tales, "orient pearls at random strung", woven into a connected narrative by a gentleman, perfectly well-known to the present generation of literary eccentrics and collectors, as having amassed one of the most remarkable collections of erotic pictures and bric-a-brac ever brought together. He was also an ardent traveller and *The Romance of Lust* was composed during a voyage he made to Japan'.

One hundred and fifty copies of the book were printed at the author-compiler's expense for friends and acquaintances, but at his death, the majority of these, remaining undistributed, were evidently destroyed, leaving but a score or so in existence in Ashbee's time.

One would have liked elucidation of Ashbee's remark that the *Romance* was 'not the produce of a single pen, but consists of several tales ... woven into a connected narrative'. Certainly the first three volumes give every sign of unity; only the last, in terms of its setting and some of its additional characters, could have thought to have been adapted from another work.

The Romance of Lust is the classic example of pornography's slaying of erotica. So far from being an aphrodisiac, it is an articulated museum piece—the prime representative of a world in which copulation becomes a maniac, mechanical *thing: das Ding an sich,* the thing itself and in itself. It is a world stripped bare of all save generative organs, where sisters and brothers, mothers and sons, uncles, aunts, nephews and nieces copulate with machine-room rhythm. It is the outsider, though not alone as such: the divorcee from the gusty lustiness of *A Night in a Moorish Harem,* the sensuality of *The Voluptuous Night,* the comparative richness of prose of *Venus in India,* the civilized mannerisms of *Evelyn,* or— at the furthest remove—the witty delicacy of Andrea de Nerciat's *Le Doctorat Impromptu**.

CHAPTER ONE

There were three of us—Mary, Eliza, and myself. I was approaching fifteen, Mary was about a year younger, and Eliza between twelve and thirteen years of age. Mamma treated us all as children, and was blind to the fact that I was no longer what I had been. Although not tall for my age, nor outwardly presenting a manly appearance, my passions were awakening, and the distinctive feature of my sex, although in repose it looked magnificent enough, was very sufficiently developed when under the influence of feminine excitement.

As yet, I had absolutely no knowledge of the uses of the different organs of sex. My sisters and I all slept in the same room, they together in one bed, I alone in another. When no one was present, we had often mutually examined the different formations of our sexes.

We had discovered that mutual handlings gave a certain amount of pleasing sensation; and, latterly, my eldest sister had discovered that the hooding and unhooding of my doodle, as she called it, instantly

---

* Translated by Dudley Leslie as *The Unexpected Love Lesson* (The Libra Collection, London, 1970).

caused it to swell up and stiffen as hard as a piece of wood. My feeling her gave rise in her to nice sensations, but on the slightest attempt to insert even my finger, the pain was too great. We had made so little progress in these *attouchements* that not the slightest inkling of what could be done in that way dawned upon us. I had begun to develop a slight growth of moss-like curls round the root of my cock; and then, to our surprise, Mary began to show a similar tendency. As yet, Eliza was as bald as her hand, but both were prettily formed, with wonderfully full and fat mounts of Venus. We were perfectly innocent of guile and quite habituated to let each other look at all our naked bodies without the slightest hesitation.

My father had left us but moderately provided for, and mamma, wishing to live comfortably, preferred giving me lessons along with my sisters at home to sending me to school; but her health beginning to fail, she inserted an advertisement in the *Times* for a governess. Out of a large number of applicants, a young lady, of the name of Evelyn, was selected. Some ten days afterwards she arrived, and became one of the family.

We did not see much of her the first evening, but after breakfast the following morning, mamma accompanied her to what was considered our school-room, and said, 'Now, my dears, I place you under Miss Evelyn's care; you must obey her in all things; she will teach you your lessons, as I am unable to do so any longer'. Then, turning to our new governess, 'I fear you will find them somewhat spoiled, and unruly; but there is a horse, and Susan will make you excellent birch rods whenever you require them. If you spare their bottoms when they deserve whipping, you will seriously offend me'. As mamma said this, I observed Miss Evelyn's eyes appeared to dilate with a sort of joy, and I felt certain that, severely as mamma had often whipped us, if we should now deserve it, Miss Evelyn would administer it much more severely. She looked amiability itself, and was truly beautiful in face and person, twenty-two years of age, full and finely formed, and dressed always with the most studied neatness. She was, in truth, a seductive creature. She made an instantaneous impression on my senses. There was, however, somewhat of a sternness of expression, and a dignity of carriage, which caused us at once to fear and respect her. Of course, at first, all went smoothly enough, and seeing that mama treated me precisely as she did my sisters, I came to be regarded as quite a child by Miss Evelyn. She found that she had to sleep in the same room with my sisters and myself. I fancied that on the first night Miss Evelyn did not approve of this arrangement, but gradually became familiarized with it, and seemed to think no more about it.

When bedtime came, we all kissed mamma and retired early, as usual. Miss Evelyn followed some hours later. When she came in, she carefully locked the door, then looked at me to see if I was asleep. Why, I know not, but I was instinctively prompted to feign sleep. I did so successfully, notwithstanding the passing of the candle before my eyes. So she at once commenced undressing. When her back was turned, I opened my eyes, and greedily devoured her naked charms as they were gradually exhibited before me. The moment she turned round, I was again as if asleep. I have said that my passions had begun to develop themselves, but as yet I did not understand their force or direction. I well remember this first night, when a fine ripe woman gradually removed every particle of dress within a couple of yards of me—the effect of each succeeding charm, from her lovely and beautifully formed bubbies to the taking of her shoes and stockings from her well-formed legs and small feet and ankles, caused my prick to swell and stiffen to a painful extent. When all but her chemise was removed, she stooped to pick up her petticoats that she had allowed to fall to her feet, and in lifting them, raised also her chemise, and exposed to my view a most glorious bottom—dazzlingly white and shining like satin. As the light was full upon it, and she was still in a stooping position, I could see that below her slit she was well covered with dark hair. Turning round, to put her petticoats on a chair, and to take up her night-gown, she slipped her chemise from her arm, and letting it fall to the ground while she lifted the night-gown over her head, I had for some seconds a view of her beautiful belly, thickly covered with dark curly hair over the mount of Venus. So voluptuous was the sight, I almost shuddered, so intense was my excitement. She now sat down on the bed to take off her shoes and stockings. Oh! what beautiful thighs, legs, ankles, and feet she had!

I am now advanced in life, and have had many handsome and well-formed women, but I never saw limbs more voluptuously formed.

I heard the charming creature get into bed, and shortly breathe hard. As for me, I could not sleep. I lay awake the greater part of the night, afraid to be restless, lest I should disturb Miss Evelyn and give her reason to think I had been observant of her undressing.

When at last I dozed off, it was but to dream of all the charms I had seen.

About a month passed thus. Every night Miss Evelyn became more and more at her ease, and confident of my mere childishness, often gave me glorious and lengthened glimpses of her beautifully developed charms: although it was only about every other night that I could enjoy them, for, as they always produced sleeplessness afterwards, the following night nature assured her rights, and I usually slept profoundly when I would infinitely have preferred continued gazing on the charms of my lovely governess. But, doubtless, those exhausting sleeps helped to throw her off her guard, and gave me better opportunities than I should otherwise have had.

In cold weather I used to sit on a low stool by the fire—Miss Evelyn was seated in front. I had my lesson book on my knee, and she herself would place her beautiful feet on the high school fender, with her work in her lap, while she heard my sisters repeat their lesson, totally unconscious that for half an hour at a time she was exposing her beautiful legs and thighs to my ardent gaze; for sitting much below her, and bending my head as if intent on my lesson my eyes were below her raised petticoats. Her close and tight-fitting white stockings displayed her well-formed legs, for while confined to the house during our morning lessons she did not wear drawers; so that in the position she sat in, with her knees higher than her feet on the already high fender, and her legs somewhat apart to hold her work in her lap more easily, the whole glorious underswell of both thighs, and the lower part of her fine large bottom, were fully exposed to my view. The light from the fire glancing under her raised petticoats tinged the whole with a glow, and set me equally in a blaze of desire until I was almost ready to faint. I could have rushed headlong under her petticoats.... Oh, how little she thought of the passion she was raising. Oh! dear Miss Evelyn, how I did love you from the dainty kid slipper and tight glossy silk stocking, up to the glorious swell of the beautiful bubbies, that were so fully exposed to me nearly every night, and the lovely lips of all that I longed to lovingly embrace.

Thus day after day passed away, and Miss Evelyn became to me a goddess, a creature whom, in my heart of hearts, I literally worshipped. When she left the school-room, and I was alone, I kissed that part of the fender her feet had pressed, and the seat on which she sat, and even the air an inch above, imagination placing there her lovely cunt. I craved for something beyond this without knowing exactly what I wanted; for, as yet, I really was utterly ignorant of anything appertaining to the conjunction of the sexes.

One day I had gone up to my sister's bedroom where the governess slept, that I might throw myself on her bed, and in imagination embrace her beautiful body. I heard some one approaching, and knowing that I had no business there, I hid myself under the bed. The next moment Miss Evelyn herself entered, and locked the door. It was about an hour before dinner. Taking off her dress, and hanging it on the wardrobe, she drew out a piece of furniture, which had been bought for her, the use of which had often puzzled me, she took off the lid, poured water into its basin, and placed a sponge near it. She then took off her gown, drew her petticoats and chemise up to her waist and fastened them there, straddled across it, and seated herself upon it.... Thus her belly, mount and thighs, whose massy-fleshed and most voluptuous shape were more fully seen by me than they had heretofore been, and it may easily be conceived into what a state such a deliberate view threw me.

When her ablutions were completed, she sat down and drew off her stockings, displaying her beautiful white calves and charming little feet. I believe it was this first admiration of the really exquisitely formed legs, ankles and feet, which were extraordinarily perfect in make, that first awakened my passion for those objects, which have since always exercised a peculiar charm over me. She was also so particularly neat in her shoes—little dark ones—that were *bijoux* to look at, I often took them up and kissed them, when left in the room. Then her silk stockings, always drawn up tight and fitting like a glove, set off to the great advantage the remarkably fine shape of her legs.

Putting on silk for cotton stockings, she took down a low-bodiced dress, finished her toilet, and left the room. I crawled out from under the bed, washed my face and hands in the water of her bidet, and even drank some in my excitement.

Some six weeks had now elapsed since the arrival of Miss Evelyn. The passion that had seized me for her had so far kept me most obedient to her slightest command, or even wish, and, from the same cause, attentive to my lessons, when not distracted by the circumstances already detailed. My example had also had the effect of keeping my sisters much in the same groove, but it was impossible this could last—it was not nature. As long as all went smoothly, Miss Evelyn seemed to be all amiability. We fancied we could do as we liked, and we grew more careless.

Miss Evelyn became more reserved, and cautioned us at first, and then threatened us with the rod. We did not think she would make use of it. Mary grew impertinent, and one afternoon turned sulky over her lessons, and set our teacher at defiance. Miss Evelyn, who had been growing more and more angry, had her rise from her seat. She obeyed with an impudent leer. Seizing her by the arm, Miss Evelyn dragged the struggling girl to the horse. My sister was strong and fought hard, using both teeth and nails, but it was to no purpose. The anger of our governess was fully roused, and raising her in her arms, she carried her forcibly to the horse, placed her on it, held her firmly with one hand while she put the noose round her with the other, which, when drawn, secured her body; other nooses secured each ankle to rings in the floor, keeping her legs apart by the projection of the horse, and also forcing the knees to bend a little, by which the most complete exposure of the bottom was obtained.

Miss Evelyn then left her, and went to mamma for a rod. In a few minutes she returned, evidently flushed with passion, and proceeded to tie Mary's petticoats well up to her waist, leaving her bottom and her pinky slit quite bare and exposed directly before my eyes.... It was in itself more exciting than I had expected, for my thoughts had so long dwelt only on the riper beauties of Miss Evelyn that I had quite ceased to have any toying with Mary.

Miss Evelyn first removed her own scarf, laying bare her plump ivory shoulders, and showing the upper halves of her beautiful bubbies, which were heaving with the excitement of her anger. She bared her fine right arm, and grasping the rod, stepped back and raised her arm; her eyes glistened in a peculiar way. She was indeed beautiful to see.

I shall never forget that moment—it was but a moment. The rod whistled through the air and fell with a cruel cut on poor Mary's plump little bottom. The flesh quivered again, and Mary, who had resolved not to cry, flushed in her face, and bit the damask with which the horse was covered.

Again the arm was raised, and again, with a sharp whistle, it fell on the palpitating buttocks below it. Still her stubborn temper bore her up, and although we saw how she winced, not a sound escaped

The Romance of Lust

from her lips. Drawing back a step, Miss Evelyn against raised her
hand and arm, and this time her aim was so true that the longer
points of the rod doubled between the buttocks. . . . So agonizing
was the pain that Mary screamed out dreadfully. Again the rod fell
precisely on the same spot.

'Oh! oh! oh! Dear, dear Miss Evelyn. I will never, no, never,
do so again'.

Her shrieks were of no avail. Cut succeeded cut, yell succeeded
yell—until the rod was worn to a stump, and poor Mary's bottom
was one mass of weals and red as raw beef. It was fearful to see, and
yet such is our nature that all this was highly exciting for me to
witness. I then and there resolved to have a closer inspection at a
more convenient opportunity, which did not fail me in the end.

Meanwhile, her spirit was completely cowed, or rather, crushed.
Indeed, we were all fully frightened, and now knew what we had to
expect, if we did not behave ourselves. There was now no fear of
any manifestation of temper, and we felt we must indeed obey
implicitly whatever our governess chose to order. We instinctively
learned to fear her.

A very few days after this memorable whipping, some visitors
arrived—a gentleman and lady. The gentleman was an old friend
of mamma's, who had late married, and mamma had asked them
to visit her on their wedding tour and spend a short time with us.

The gentleman was a fine-looking man, tall and powerfully built;
the lady rather delicate looking, but well shaped, with good breasts
and shoulders, small waist, and spreading haunches, well-formed
arms, small hands and feet, and very brilliant eyes.

I think it was about three days after their arrival that one afternoon I went into the spare room, which was occupied by these
visitors; while there, I heard them coming upstairs. The lady
entered first, and I had just time to slip into a closet and draw the
door to; it was not quite closed, but nearly so. In a minute the
gentleman followed, and gently shutting the door, locked it. Mrs.
Benson smiled, and said—

'Well, my love, you are a sad teaser; you let me have no rest.
Surely, you had enough last night and this morning without wanting
it again so soon?'

'Indeed, I had not. I never can have enough of your delicious
person. So come, we must not be long about it, or our absence will
be observed'.

He seized her round the waist, and drew her lips to his, and gave her a long, long kiss; squeezing her to him, and moving himself against her. Then seating himself, he pulled her on his knee, and thrust his hands up her petticoats, their mouths being glued together for some time.

He got up, and lifted her on the edge of the bed, threw her back, and taking her legs under his arms, exposed everything to my view.....

Rosa Fielding

ILLIAM Dugdale, the most notorious of publisher-booksellers of pornography of his time, issued this novel in 1867 under the title *The Victim of Lust! or Scenes in the Life of Rosa Fielding. Depicting the Crimes and Follies of High Life and the Dissipation and Debauchery of the Day.*

Noting, as often with Dugdale's catchpenny and rubbishy productions, '8 obscene, coloured lithographs, very badly executed', Ashbee dismissed the book as 'very obscene ... possesses no literary merit whatever'. Why he chose to dismiss it in this way is a mystery; he was wrong. *Rosa Fielding* as a novel *qua* novel is as well written and constructed as any of its time, and better than most. There is little of that puerility of construction which betrays the total amateur, as in *Rosa Rogers;* indeed the technique of creating vignettes of characters and incidents in some of the chapters arouses the occasional thought that a writer of some talent might have waywardly produced this 'one-off' piece of wicked nonsense.

CHAPTER I

It was a fine morning in May, and the dull, little-frequented High
Street of the small country town called Rutshole seemed absolutely
cheerful, as if inspired by the exhilarating atmosphere.

So at least thought Mr. Bonham, a portly widower of fifty or
thereabouts, as having left his carriage at the inn, he proceeded down
the High Street, leisurely, but with the usual solemnity on his
countenance (which he considered dignified and respectable) much
lightened by the cheering weather. He stopped at the door of a small
shop, on which was inscribed, 'Trabb, Hosier and Glover'. Here he
entered.

Now that capital woman of business, the widow Trabb, was at
that moment engaged in suiting a stiff-necked old maid with a pair
of mittens: but if she had not been so occupied, we very much
doubt if she would herself have attended to a gentleman customer.
The worthy woman knew that there are other means of making a
shop attractive besides the excellence and cheapness of the wares
therein sold; and she had enlisted in her service a pretty girl of
sixteen, whose remarkable grace and modesty had already attracted
numerous young squires, young farmers, and officers from the neighbouring garrison town, as real or pretended customers, to the manifest
advantage of Mrs. Trabb's till. When therefore, she saw the rich
and respectable Mr. Bonham enter her shop, she summoned her
aide-de-camp with, 'Rosa, attend to the gentleman!' and continued
her attention to her then customer. Now Mr. Bonham, though
nearly fifty as we have said, and of a very staid and even strict
outward demeanour, was by no means so elderly in his feelings and
physical capabilities as would have been judged from outward
appearances. He had been early left a widower, and the very fact
of his having to keep up the said outward appearances, and his
ambition to have a somewhat saintly character among his neighbours
and friends, had forced him to restrain his indulgences within very
narrow bounds, and to be circumspect and moderate in the enjoyment thereof. So that this self-denial was of a double benefit to him:
among the saints of his acquaintance he was esteemed as 'one of
the elect,' and a 'babe of grace,' while he himself was pleasingly
conscious that, thanks to his regular but very generous diet, and his
habits of self-control (not abstinence), as to the softer sex, he was
enjoying what is called a green old age; and was, when on the verge

of fifty, pretty confident that his latent powers when called into action would be found quite equal to those of many a worn-out young roué of five and twenty.

He was remarkably struck with Rosa's beauty, and well he might be. Long, flowing, golden hair; deep blue eyes; a sweet, but by no means insipid expression of face, combined with a graceful figure, and manners very attractive even in her humble occupation; all these detained Mr. Bonham longer in purchasing a pair of gloves than he had ever been in his life before. Certainly he was very difficult to suit; and Rosa had to take the measure of his hand more than once. At last he was suited—as far as gloves were concerned—and was about to leave the shop when a bright idea struck him. He turned back to where Mrs. Trabb was standing: that estimable woman had just got rid of her Low Church-looking customer triumphantly; she had clapped twopence extra on to the price of the mits, and then after some bargaining submitted to bate a penny. So both parties were satisfied, and Mrs. T. felt not only 'at peace with all men,' (that she generally was) but 'with all women' too, (which was not so frequently the case).

'Mrs. Trabb,' began the respectable gentleman, 'I should like to consult you about a little matter of business that may be a source of lawful gain to a tradeswoman in your line; besides being conducive to the moral benefit of a tribe of benighted heathens'.

'Dear Mr. Bonham,' exclaimed the gratified hosier, 'step this way —very kind of you, I'm sure—glass of cherry brandy?—do now— and sit down and rest yourself!'

So saying, she ushered the artful old gentleman into her snug back parlour; and producing the refreshment alluded to, awaited further disclosures.

We will not weary the reader with a full account of the proposed mercantile operation. Suffice it to say that Mr. Bonham disclosed a case of soul-harrowing destitution among the Fukkumite Islanders recently converted to Christianity.

The interesting females had not the wherewithal to cover their bare bottoms, but used to display those well-rounded features to the unhallowed gaze of the unregenerate sailors of the whale-ships call- ing at the islands. Now the missionaries considered that if any bottoms were to be displayed by their precious converts the exhibi- tion should be made in private to their spiritual advisers. And to end the story, the benevolent gentleman, by way of advancing the moral and physical comforts of the Fukkumite ladies, (to say nothing of the missionaries) asked Mrs. Trabb if she would like to contract for the supply of say to begin with, one thousand pairs of frilled pantalettes.

'Really very kind of you, Mr. Bonham, to give me such a chance,' said the gratified shopkeeper, 'but may I ask you, sir, if the creatures, or converts, or whatever it is most proper to call them, are to wear nothing else but these trousers?'

'No, I believe not,' was the answer. 'Why?'

'Because, sir,' replied the experienced widow, 'women's pants are made, to speak plainly, with openings at the front and rear, corresponding to her natural openings; so really, though I shall be very happy to undertake the contract, I must tell you beforehand, for fear of having my goods thrown back on my hands, that the garments proposed are no obstruction whatever to a man who is determined to violate the woman'.

'Very proper of you to make the remark, Mrs. Trabb; very businesslike and fair; but then of course the women should have opportunities for performing their natural functions conveniently; and then our dear self-sacrificing brethren the missionaries! they must have facilities for their little comforts'.

'Oh, of course, sir,' was the response.

'Then send in your estimates, Mrs. Trabb, I'll see that you have a good chance. By the by, Mrs. Trabb, who is that modest-looking and rather attractive young person who attended to my requirements just now in your shop?'

('Aha!' thought the sharp widow, 'that's it, eh? Rather caught, I should think'.)

'That young woman, sir, is a daughter of the Fieldings. You know, sir, farmers about three miles from here. Rosa her name is— a very nice girl, and as good as she looks. Take another glass, sir!'

'No, thank you, Mrs. Trabb, send in those estimates as soon as you can, and good-day to you'.

Exit Bonham.

The very next morning he mounted his fine weight-carrying cob, and riding out leisurely as if for exercise, had no sooner got out of sight and hearing of Rutsden Lodge, as his residence was termed, and out of the ken of his sharp daughter Eliza, than he spurred his good hackney into a smart trot, which pace being occasionally varied by a canter, very soon brought him to Elm-Tree Farm.

Farmer Fielding was out, which his visitor was not altogether very sorry for, as he thought it would be better in every way to begin his tactics by talking the old lady over. She received him very kindly and hospitably, though evidently puzzled to know the object of his visit. Mr. Bonham was not long in breaking ground, for he knew the farmer might return in five minutes. He recounted to the gratified mother how he had been struck by the elegant yet modest and quiet appearance of Rosa, and how he was pleased to learn from Mrs. Trabb, that she was as good as she looked; that notwithstanding the great respectability of Mrs. T. and her establishment, and the high opinion he had of her moral worth, still he could not but be aware that a position behind her counter was pernicious, if not absolutely dangerous, to a girl of Rosa's attractive personal qualities.

'Why, my dear madam,' urged the moralist, 'I am informed that the young squires and farmers will ride a couple of miles out of their way to deal in Mrs. Trabb's shop; and then those dragoon officers come all the way from Baboonfield Barracks. I know that man of Moab, their colonel, Earl Phuckumthefirst, gets all his clothes from London, and I'd like to know what he wants at Mrs. Trabb's in Rutshole High Street!'

'Perhaps dear Rosy may make a good marriage,' simpered the fond and foolish mother.

'Perhaps, madam,' interposed Mr. Bonham sternly, 'she may learn something about what ought to come after marriage, but never before. How would you like to hear of her bolting off to London with one of those swells who perhaps is married already, and her returning to you in about twelve months, neglected, sick and heartbroken, with a baby in her arms? Now listen to me, Mrs. Fielding,' continued Mr. Bonham, gazing attentively in the good dame's horror-stricken face; 'I am not too old to have my fancies; and, what is more, I can afford to pay for my fancies. Moreover, my daughter will soon be married and off my hands, and I have no one else to interfere with me'.

With this introduction, the modest gentleman proposed a scheme of his own, namely that Rosa should be placed at a first-rate school in the neighbourhood of London; that all the expenses, including her equipment, should be borne by him; and that in twelve or eighteen months, if Rosa had been well-behaved and steady, and had improved in body and mind as there was every reason to suppose she would, he, the speaker, would make her Mrs. Bonham, and mistress of Rutsden Lodge.

This grand proposition fairly took away the good old lady's breath; and there is no doubt but that her reply would have been a ready acceptance of Mr. Bonham's proposition, but then there appeared old Fielding, and the whole story had to be commenced over again.

He did not receive Mr. Bonham's offer so enthusiastically as his wife had done; but he owned at the same time the risk that Rosa ran in her present situation; and in plain blunt speech detailed how Susan Shufflebum had been seen behind a hayrack with her legs over young Squire Rootlepole's back.

'And I suppose, missus,' continued the worthy man, 'I needn't tell ye what he was a-doing to her; and Harriette Heavely went a-walking in Snugcroft Woods with one of those danged soger officers, and when she got home her white petticoat was all green with damp grass, and she was so sore between her thighs that she has not been able to walk rightly since. But still Master Bonham, although your proposal would take our Rosa out of the way of danger; leastways out of a good deal, for a young, good-looking lass is never to stay quite out of danger, yet I don't quite like her being brought up above her station; she'll maybe look down on her old father and mother, and maybe she'll be looked down upon and made to feel the difference by them that's born of better families'.

This sensible speech of Farmer Fielding's was combated pretty sharply by the other two parties to the conversation; the old woman being anxious to see her daughter made a rich lady, and loath to miss the present chance, and Mr. Bonham, continuing to urge that his being almost entirely without relations and that his daughter being about to be married, would place Rosa in a far different and much more pleasant situation than is usually the case under such circumstances. He even went on to say that although Fielding had a right to deal as he liked with regard to his own daughter, yet he considered it would be almost sinful for him to throw away such a good chance of having her well educated and married, and that too in the fear of the Lord. Half badgered to death between the pair of them—the old farmer yielded a reluctant consent, upon which Mr. Bonham and Mrs. Fielding went at once into matters of detail with regard to preparation of an outfit and so on.

One thing was determined upon; that the matter might not be talked about more than was absolutely necessary, Mr. Bonham in particular being anxious to conceal his philanthropic schemes from his daughter Eliza, lest peradventure she had been addicted to wrath.

And Farmer Fielding thought that the less said about Rosa, until she appeared as Mrs. Bonham, the better.

We do not intend to weary our readers as to matters of outfit; suffice it to say that Mrs. Trabb was in high glee, and began to think that Mr. Bonham, what with his missionary zeal on behalf of the sweet Fukkumite savages, and his philanthropic intentions regarding Rosa's welfare was going to make her fortune. Certainly she never had had two such orders in one twelvemonth, much less in one week. One remark of hers to Mr. Bonham is worthy of notice.

With the natural sharpness of a woman and a widow to boot, she took it for granted that Mr. B. would like to know some particulars about the undergarments she had been furnishing for his pretty protégée, and after expatiating for an hour or so about silk stockings, cotton stockings, chemises, night-dresses, petticoats, and the Lord only knows what besides, she concluded with:

'And I quite remember your sensible remarks, Mr. Bonham, about those trousers made for those converted cannibals. Miss Rosa's are much finer of course, and prettier altogether; but they are equally convenient! they are quite open back and front'.

This remark was made with a good deal of emphasis and meaning. But the venerable philanthropist merely replied, without moving a muscle of his face:

'You are quite right, Mrs. Trabb, and have acted very judiciously; one never knows what may be required in case of emergency!'

It was reported to a few friends and neighbours that Rosa was offered a situation in London as a nursery governess and that as Mr. Bonham was going to town on business he had kindly offered to convey the young lady thither in his own carriage; being as he said, altogether safer and pleasanter for a young unprotected girl than the public conveyance. This excuse passed currently enough, and if some of the envious or captious neighbours shook their heads, and said old Bonham was a sly fox, what business was it of theirs after all?

Rosa enjoyed the ride immensely. Her guardian, as she took to calling him, was so kind, and so affectionate, (the fact was that he kept kissing her a great many times, and much more warmly than there was any occasion for) that she considered herself a very fortunate girl. And then he took such an interest in minor matters; he wanted to know how Mrs. Trabb had executed his orders—with regard to her wardrobe—and in his anxiety to know if everything was nice and proper, actually commenced to investigate Rosa's

M

underclothing. He expressed his opinion that the petticoats would do; but that the outer one was hardly fine enough, but that defect could be repaired in London; his research became more interesting when the chemise was put upon its trial.

'And now, Rosa darling,' said the ancient voluptuary, 'let me see if Mrs. Trabb has obeyed my orders about your trousers. I told her that you were to have them made in a certain way, or to wear none at all!'

'Oh, dear me, Mr. Bonham!' exclaimed Rosa, who all this time had been dutifully holding up her clothes to facilitate her guardian's explorations, 'you will make me ashamed of myself!'

'Not at all, my dear girl,' was the reassuring reply, 'it is my duty to see that you have everything nice and proper, and your duty to submit to the inquiry; so put your graceful right leg over my left shoulder'.

Trembling and blushing, the innocent girl, fancying that it was not quite right and yet not knowing very well how to refuse, did as she was requested, and made a splendid exposure of her secret parts immediately.

'Ha!' exclaimed Bonham, 'I see that Mrs. Trabb has not neglected her duty; your trousers are well open in front certainly, though for the sake of seeing your thighs I would have preferred no trousers at all.

'As you are going to be married to me in twelve or eighteen months, my lovely Rosa, I regard you already as my wife, morally speaking, and if the jolting of this carriage will allow I will give you a practical proof of it'.

'A practical proof, sir!' stammered Rosa.

'Yes, my beloved child'.

* * * * *

Robert pursued his way towards the farmhouse, which he never would have had the slightest difficulty in finding without any guidance; secretly congratulating himself that whether he succeeded or not, in doing any business for his master, he had managed a very nice little bit of amusement for himself. So far, so good. Entering the farmhouse, he at once accosted a jolly-looking dame, whom he correctly enough supposed to be Mother Fielding, asked permission to sit down, and the favour of a draught of milk.

The old lady perceiving at once from his neat, plain groom's dress, and the cockade in his hat, that he was some superior gentleman's servant, and propitiated probably by his good looks, not only asked him to rest himself, but put before him a tankard of strong ale, and some bread and cheese; remarking that it would be hard if Fielding's farm could not afford a tired stranger a mouthful of beer.

'Then this is Fielding's farm, is it?' said the apparently astonished Robert, 'and you are Mrs. Fielding, the mother of that beautiful young lady the officers at the barracks are always talking about'.

Mrs. Fielding acknowledged that she was the mother of the young lady in question, not without a deal of conscious pride at hearing Rosa so described; remarking, however, that it was like the officers' impudence to be so free in talking about her daughter.

'But I suppose,' concluded the old lady, 'it is all the same to them, my daughter, or anybody else's!'

'Truly madam, I fear you are not far wrong,' said the moral Robert, 'and our young gentlemen are rather too free both in their conversation and manners; but in the case of so very distinguished a beauty as I hear Miss Fielding is, a little talk comes natural. Besides, madam, in this case it is quite excusable, as report does say your daughter is going to make a high marriage'.

'People should mind their own business, and not tell lies about other folks' affairs,' said Mrs. Fielding, prudently remembering Mr. Bonham's admonitions on the subjects of silence and secrecy.

'Ah, well, if it is a lie,' replied the acute Robert, making his point at once, 'I'll contradict it—whenever I hear it—and mention my authority'.

'Not but what Rose could be if she chose,' interposed the old dame, 'of course such things are generally unlikely'.

'Very unlikely,' here interrupted Robert, in order to irritate her, and lead her on.

'But there are exceptions to every rule, and my girl Rosa, who is as good as she is pretty, may be an exception in this case. Mind, I don't say she is!'

'Oh, of course not!' interposed the military groom, 'and that's the reason she has gone to London, I suppose!'

'Why not exactly to be married,' replied Mrs. Fielding; forgetting all about concealment, in her own self-satisfaction, and drawn on by her guest's confident manner, 'not to be married just yet. You see, though Rosa has been well brought up, yet a little London polish is desirable to fit her for the high station she will occupy'.

'Oh, of course!' replied Robert, in a matter-of-fact way, as if he knew all about it, and highly approved, but thinking to himself all the while:

'You are a nice soft old lady, and if you let out this secret to everyone as easily as you have let it out to me, it will very soon be parish news. But your ale is good at any rate, so here's to your good health, ma'am!'

This last remark was uttered aloud, and politely acknowledged.

'Oh, I'm afraid you are a dreadful set up at the barracks, young man. You are in service to one of the gentlemen, I see. Pray, who may he be?'

'Only acting as officer's servant, madam,' replied her guest, 'you know the officers are at liberty to choose the smartest and best-looking—ahem!—of the men, to act as servants for them'.

'Certainly,' said the farmer's wife, 'why not? And who are you with at present?'

All this interlude gave Robert time for invention, so accordingly out he came, with one of the biggest lies he ever told in his life—and that is saying a good deal.

'Major Ringtail, madam, of the 51st Dragoons, is the gentleman I am with. He drove over to Rutshole this morning, and as he did not want me to assist him in the business he was after, he gave me a holiday; which I thought I could not employ more innocently than by a walk in the country'.

'Quite right, young man,' replied the old lady, 'and what sort of a man is the major?'

'Oh, he's a very nice quiet sort of a gentlemanly man,' was the reply, 'he's rather addicted to gambling and drinking, but then you know, Mrs. Fielding, that officers at country quarters must amuse themselves somehow—and he may be said by strict people to be damnably given to cursing and swearing and fighting. Indeed, the Reverend Brother Stiggins said so the other day, when the Major kicked him out of the barrack yard. But then, you know madam, men will be stupid and aggravating; and fools like Stiggins will interfere where they have no business. And people do say of my respected master—people will talk, you know—that he spends too much of his valuable time in fornication; and that he is over much given to rogering any of the pretty country lasses, or any other girls that he may happen to fall in with. But I suppose he considers that proceeding to be part of his duty, as an officer of H.M.'s 51st

Dragoons. And,' said Robert, in conclusion, 'considering that he is a dragoon officer, I think he behaves himself on the whole as well as can be expected'.

'On the hole,' said Mrs. Fielding to herself, 'well perhaps he does. I wonder how he behaves off the hole!' But she only said: 'Pray, young man, what did that respectable gentleman, your master, kick the sainted Brother Stiggins out of the barracks for? I think that holy man was terribly indiscreet in venturing to trust his sainted body in such a den of iniquity. But I beg your pardon, young man, I did not mean to hurt your feelings; the words slipped out unawares'.

'Well, madam,' said Robert, gravely, 'we don't generally call the barracks a den of iniquity. You see, perhaps our gentlemen might not understand what that meant, but it is commonly known by the name of Hell's Blazes; and Mrs. Mantrap, the colonel's lady—his wife's at Cheltenham—calls it Little Sodom. But that's neither here nor there,' continued the narrator with a side glance at his hostess' horror-stricken countenance, 'you were asking me about that little unpleasantness between the major and that apostle Stiggins. I know all about it; for you see the major had got me with him in case of Stiggins, or any of the congregation turning nasty'.

'What! were you in the chapel?' asked the old lady, in great surprise. 'And what were you doing there?'

'We went to Little Bethel Chapel, madam, to offer up our devotions to the best of our ability,' replied Robert demurely. 'You see in the tenth pew from the pulpit, on the left-hand side, a deuced nice girl used to sit, and in the afternoon, generally by herself. I told my master, as in duty bound, and he was taken with a pious fit. So he found out who the girl was, and after speaking to her two or three times in the street in the most impudent way, he pretends that she has converted him—ha, ha!—and says that he should like to be gathered into the fold, the only fold he was thinking of being the folds of her petticoats. Well, ma'am, I don't think she could be quite such a fool as to believe all he said, but what with having her brain softened with Stiggins' nonsensical saintly trash, and what with the pride of showing off a dragoon officer as a brand saved from the burning in her own pew: and perhaps a little feeling of another kind besides—you know what I mean, Mrs. F.—all combined together to induce her to make a fool of herself, and she made an appointment with the major to meet in her pew one Sunday afternoon, when her mother would be asleep at home, and her father smoking his pipe. All this my master told me, of course, for I was to stick to him, and what's more I got a special chum of mine, Tom, Lieutenant Larkyns' man, to come with me and sit pretty close, for you see madam, there was no telling how the congregation, to say nothing of the deacons and elders, and that bad lot, might take it'.

'Take it! Take what?' exclaimed Mrs. Fielding.

'Patience, madam, and you shall hear,' replied Robert, with drunken gravity, for the strong ale was beginning to take effect upon him. 'During the first part of Stiggins' mountebanking, his prayers, and howlings, and damning everybody but himself up hill and down dale, my master behaved himself tolerably quiet; merely kissing Miss Larcher, (that's her name) every now and then, giving her an occasional squeeze, and putting his hand up her petticoats in a devotional manner when they knelt down together'.

'Good Lord!' interrupted the farmer's wife, 'do you call that behaving quietly?'

'Very much so indeed, madam,' was the reply, 'not a sound was to be heard in the pig-market—I beg pardon: Chapel—except the bawling of that Stiggins who howled enough for sixty. His bawling had one good effect at any rate; it sent half his disciples to sleep before he had got to tenthly, and when he arrived at thirteenthly, all the older part, and half of the congregation were snoring comfortably. Not so my master and his fair friend. I had noticed him getting on very favourably. Once he laid her backwards on the seat, and took a regular good, long, groping feel at her privates. I had been stooping down below the level of the door of the pew to get a good suck at a flask of brandy and water, which I had brought with me, to enable me to bear up against the fatigue and to bring myself into a devotional frame of mind, when, on raising my eyes, the first thing I saw was a pair of remarkably good legs, nicely set off by clean white stockings, and neat little shoes, showing over the side of the adjoining pew. Of course, I knew what such an apparition as this meant, and if I couldn't guess, I was very soon enlightened, for on quietly peeping over the edge—as was my duty, in order to see that all was straightfoward and pleasant—there I saw my respected and gallant master fucking, as the common people term it, Miss Larcher in a most splendid style.

'But do you mean to tell me, young man,' interrupted Mrs. Fielding, 'that none of the congregation noticed what was going on?'

'One of them did, Mrs Fielding,' coolly replied the narrator, 'but, as he came towards the pew, I told him that it was the case of a female in a severe spiritual conflict with Satan, and that if he didn't go back to his seat, I'd make him, and that damned quick. So he went, apparently quite convinced. And as for the rest of the congregation, they were either asleep or stupid, as of course they naturally must be to come to such a stinking hole at all! so my master buttoned his trousers in peace, and his pretty friend adjusted her dress, and they marched out, before Stiggins had nearly finished his yelling. But the brute from the top of his sentry-box, which he calls a watch-tower, had the advantage of overlooking the sleeping-pens of his flock, and great was his disgust, as you may imagine, on perceiving a fine young ram like my master getting into the mutton of a pretty ewe lamb, like Miss Larcher. And he came to the barracks, firstly to threaten the major with hell-fire, which he seems to know a good deal about—secondly to endeavour on finding the major did not seem to care very much about the flames, to get a ten-pound note out of him, by way of a bribe for holding his tongue. Then, on finding that the major did not care one damn whether he held his tongue or not, and did not propose to give him any money, he changed his tone once more, and told the major if he did not give him ten, or fifteen pounds, he would tell Miss Larcher's father and mother, and would have her turned out of the congregation of the saints, completely disgraced. Upon this, the major informed him, that he, the saintly Stiggins, had been discovered in a pigsty rogering a young sow; that he, the major, had half-a-dozen witnesses quite ready to prove it, and that if he annoyed him, or Miss Larcher with his blackguard lies, he would have him up before the magistrates for bestiality. And before the horror-stricken Stiggins could recover his presence of mind on hearing this intelligence, he found himself being kicked out of the barracks with speed and dexterity, and I have no doubt it did him a power of good.

'And now, Mrs. Fielding, with many thanks for your kind hospitality, I must say good-bye. If you had another daughter at home, I would ask for an introduction, but as it is, I must do without. Duty calls, madam, farewell!'

So saying, the half-drunken Robert took his departure to report progress to his master, leaving Mrs. Fielding lifting up her hands and eyes, as she exclaimed:

'Good Lord—a—mussy me!'

Sheaves from an
Old Escritoire

HIS little monster of the later Victorian era, appearing under the imprint of Henry Robinson, Fleet Street, 1897, typifies the several similar works (*Rosa Rogers* is another) in which total naivety of style and construction is clothed in every typographical nicety. It is the sort of haphazard story which a hack journalist would be capable of writing in about three days given a pile of similar books at his elbow from which he could contrive a pastiche. Thus in the Epping Forest scene here included, one is reminded, as perhaps was the author, of one of the episodes in de Sade's *Justine,* though no cruelty occurs with the paper figure of Norah.

Sheaves from an Old Escritoire is a type of book of its period which was either the end result of a quick back-room commission by a printer-publisher of clandestine books with a growing circle of clients, or a story produced in attempted emulation of others which the 'proud author' may have caused to have printed for self satisfaction and private circulation, as was, according to Ashbee, the case with *The Romance of Lust.* This would distinguish it from such titles as *The New Ladies' Tickler* or *Susan Aked* which were almost certainly voluntary creative efforts for which the authors would eventually have found a commercial publisher during preparation or on completion.

CHAPTER EIGHT

The morning after the events related in the last chapter, the little servant knocked at Norah's bedroom and opened the door. She observed the young lady lying in a dishevelled state in a deep sleep, and going up to her she pulled the sheet over her uncovered body.

This only caused Norah to turn round and stretch out her arms with a few muttered words of endearment, but when she opened her eyes and saw who was there she sat up and asked the girl whether she looked all right.

'Oh, Miss Norah, you do look blue under the eyes, and tired. What have you been doing?'

'I have been awake half the night. But you looked very washed out, too. What have you been doing, you naughty girl?'

'It is your wicked brother's fault. He crept into my room last night, and would not let me any rest'.

After giving some details of what had occurred, the girl went downstairs, and Norah began to dress and to form a plan in her own mind how to run away with her lover. Bob had left her before six o'clock after a night spent in all the delights that could be crowded in to the few short hours; and before leaving they had agreed to force matters by making a runaway match, and resolved upon making a flight to London.

After breakfast she confided her secret to her brother, and they arranged matters with such success, that the next morning found Bob and his companion in a small boarding house in London. He had enough money to last them until something could be done to reconcile his angry parent; but meantime their chief anxiety was to be able to remain quite hidden from all their friends and belongings.

With this view, he only permitted a stay of a couple of days in London, and the third day they started for a small village close to Epping Forest.

Leaving their small amount of luggage at the station, they spent the morning in exploring the Forest, which was quite unknown to both. About mid-day they stopped at an old-fashioned thatched cottage, where they enjoyed a welcome meal, provided by a kindly looking woman, who set a table under a chestnut tree, assisted by a pretty looking daughter. The meal finished, they asked if it was possible for them to have a room for a few days. The woman agreed to lodge and board them, but said they would have to rough it, to which they made no objection.

She then told them a number of stories about the rough characters who came from London and prowled about in search of what they could get by robbing, and especially about the blackmailers who pounced upon any couple they could find walking about under the trees, and who would demand money or threaten to accuse them of committing indecent actions in the public footpaths.

She also told them that only three weeks ago she had been alarmed because her daughter had not come in as usual with the cow, which grazed in the Forest and had to be brought in every night and morning for milking. Her husband started off in search when he came in from work, and after a long hunt, he heard the tinkle of the bell which was tied round the neck of their cow. Running in that direction he observed the cow standing by a fallen trunk and a white figure lying close against the tree.

He found to his horror that it was his poor girl, lying stark naked, tied with her hands behind her to the tree, and gagged. She was in a fainting condition, but when he had unbound her and wrapped his coat round her, she came to her senses. She told him that she was driving the cow home when two men and a dark woman, like a gipsy, had come up and seized her. The woman had a large bottle of spirits, and they were all half drunk. They quickly gagged her mouth to stop her cries, and the woman carrying away her clothes left her naked in the hands of the two ruffians who had taken it in turns to abuse her, and that after she had undergone two or three attacks from each, they had decamped.

The mother told Norah that she knew the men very well, but did not dare complain, as they would be sure to attack her old man and would bring others of the gang to swear they were in quite another place at the time.

There had also been many complaints from innocent young men and women, who had been set upon by this gang. Some had been allowed to go, on giving up all their money and jewellery, and others had been illtreated because they had nothing of any value—the girls having to submit to any liberties that the roughs might desire —some, who had always made their young men keep within the bounds of decency, having to allow their virgin charms to be defiled by the bullies one after another.

Norah was deeply interested in all this and Bob was thinking what weapons and precautions he should take, when the daughter ran by the table and whispered—Here come two!—and escaped into the house.

Just then three men dressed like harvesters, but splendidly built, came in at the little gate and asked for some ginger beer. Norah felt quite a trembling thrill run through her, as she saw each man give her a searching look, and she found herself almost fascinated at the thought of being in the power of these magnificent males.

The men who seemed to have plenty of money in spite of their rough exterior, sat down at another rustic table and began talking about prize fighting and racing. Then they turned and spoke to Bob about the weather, asking him if he was stopping any time and telling him of some show places in the forest that he must not miss.

After they had rested awhile, they took their departure.

The hostess, in the meantime, had got the room ready for the young couple, and now invited Norah inside to look at the accommodation. When they had got upstairs, she told Norah that the men had been eyeing her closely and whispering, and she added that she hoped she would not be frightened, but they could have plenty of rambles without any fear of danger if they kept to the known paths.

After tea the lovers had a stroll; and, as Bob was complaining of a sick headache, they retired early and passed a quiet night. Norah being disturbed by visions of adventures with ruffians.

The next morning found Bob unable to get up and obliged to stop in bed with a bilious attack.

The early part of the day passed quietly and when the time came for bringing in the cow, Norah, who had made her companion as comfortable as possible, offered to go with the daughter.

They started through the Forest, and went to the places where the cow usually grazed, but could see no signs of her. Norah was gradually getting alarmed, and kept asking the girl if she was sure of the way.

All at once they heard a rustling noise and a sound of breaking through the thick undergrowth, and the next moment the three men who had stopped at the cottage the day before, burst into view, and the leader, taking off his hat, addressed Norah.

'Pardon me, Miss, but I am the chief of the real owners of this part of the Forest and as you are trespassing on my domain you must pay toll'.

Norah, who was trembling with fear and excitement, answered that she had only a few shillings.

'This will never do,' said the bandit. And without more ado the three men quickly gagged her and the girl, who had become speechless through fright, and proceeded to undo their clothes and search them.

After taking a watch and chain and the small money Norah carried with her, the Chief said: 'I am afraid, Miss, that the property you possess between your thighs must make amends for what is short in your pocket'. And with that they threw off their coats and arranged a covering on the moss, and Norah found herself stretched on her back.

The leader now having let his trousers fall, put away all his roughness and gently passed his hand up Norah's legs. She began to make a virtue of necessity, and ceased making any violent opposition. As her conqueror saw a gleam in her eyes which was not altogether of anger, he whispered—'Make the best of it, my darling, and I will let you be ungagged if you promise not to call out'. As she nodded her head, he undid the handkerchief, and soon he felt responsive throbs and thrusts answering to his penetrating plunges.

'Here's a go'—he cried. 'The toff's lady is a treat, she's almost as tight as those two school misses we blocked last Monday!'

Norah at this moment was plunging in ecstasy, and, regardless of all modest feeling, she pressed her lips to the lips of the chief while she sent an effusion which effectually lubricated his monstrous machine. The next moment a flood gate seemed to burst and she felt his stream forced into her very womb.

Hardly had the mighty tool retired, when the place was filled by number two, who soon brought on a second spasm, while the chief renewed his acquaintance with the rosy charms of the cottager's daughter, who was persuaded to take her part of the enjoyment when her possessor had assured her that her friend was really enjoying herself.

After all three men had left well satisfied with these two samples of female beauty, Norah made the young girl promise to say nothing, and they regained the cottage with the cow, keeping the adventure of the afternoon to themselves.

Bob was much better; and not being in the secret, he was ignorant of the comparisons which were drawn by his companion between his capabilities, and those of the Forest giants.

* * * * *

Having made the most of a week's stay in the forest, Norah and Bob were anxious to get the marriage through, and this was managed during a visit which they made to Windsor, and shortly after the ceremony Norah sent a few lines to her friend Marion, which was answered by return of post with an invitation for them both to come and stay a few nights with her.

So they set off, and arrived at Marion's house one afternoon. She was alone when they arrived, but the two young ladies had much to talk about concerning their recent experiences, and left Bob having a smoke downstairs.

After a cup of tea, Marion began to talk about her honeymoon, but Norah remarked that she had seen the account in Marion's letters to Mlle, which had been forwarded to her.

Shortly after this Marion's husband made his appearance and in him Bob immediately recognized his old chum to whom he had written the confidential letter about his meeting with Norah; but having no idea that he should find him again under the present circumstances.

They were all soon in a most delightful state of intimacy. The evening passed with a great deal of joking and allusions to what would happen if by chance the pairs got disarranged.

The following day the relations became still closer and at night Norah challenged Marion to a bolster match which came off on the landing. Marion was bigger, but not so active, and as they fought in their nightdresses Norah gave Marion a blow on the shoulder which pulled off a button at the neck, so that she was obliged to use one hand, causing her to be easily beaten. She was, therefore, to receive three smacks on the bare bottom from Bob.

They were obliged to be quiet for fear of waking up the servant, and while Marion was paying her forfeit, Norah exchanged some artful glances with Charlie, who disappeared to turn off the gas and left all in darkness. Then he crept up to Norah and led her into his room, leaving the other pair to shift for themselves.

Having lifted her on the bed, he got in beside her and for a few seconds they lay locked in each other's arms. She soon returned his ardent kisses, while he fondled and praised her bubbies, his hands wandering over her luscious thighs; at last a finger penetrated to her voluptuous little cleft, wet with excitement, and she heaved a sigh and murmured—'Leave off, you bad boy!'

He was soon tenderly feeling the delightful grotto, which made her open her thighs and entwine her legs round his buttocks.

'Now darling, let me get on top of you'—he said—'There. Now I will be very gentle'.

She then opened her lily-white thighs, and pulled her chemise up over her bubbies. He was soon on the top of this luscious object, Norah helping. Then the gentle sinous motion of their bodies began, her legs twined round his back, her arms pressing him to her, her lips to his; their bodies thrilled with every gentle thrust, low moans of pleasure came from her, purrings of suppressed delight, faster and faster grew their thrusts ... One ... two ... three concentrated pushes; they both gasp as the rich liquor of love shoots from him into her palpitating womb, and with a satisfied happiness both sink on the bed exhausted.

The following morning the hosts and guests met at breakfast in rather a shame-faced manner, as the wanderings of the erring couples had led to great confusion, and during a great part of the night all four had been lying together, so that what had begun as an innocent bolster match terminated in an orgie. However the succeeding days passed away pleasantly enough in a repetition of the same pleasant scenes.

The Simple Tale of
Susan Aked

HE original title page of
this unusual little book announces itself as, *And* (sic) *Instructive
Story, The Simple Tale of Susan Aked, or Innocence Awakened,
Ignorance Dispelled*. The date is given as 1898, which is probably
correct, under the not infrequent imprint of The Erotika Biblion
Society of London and New York.

As with *The Force of Instinct* in *The Bagnio Miscellany*, this
story is based on the conversational plan of *The Dialogues of Luisa
Sigea*, with equal nods undoubtedly to Aretino's *Ragionamenti* and
Lucian's *Dialogues of the Courtesans*. What renders Susan Aked a
particularly unusual heroine is that she is instructed by her friend
Lucia in birth control methods of the time—primarily by use of a
'sponge of very fine texture' attached to 'a rose-coloured silken
thread', the sponge being soaked in 'a mixture of carbonized oil,
glycerine and a little rose water to give it a pleasant smell'. The
syringe is mentioned, as are sheaths, but Lucia explains the preferred physical use of the sponge on much the same grounds as are
expressed today in relation to the use of the Pill.

Heroines of Pornotopia are normally never subject to pregnancies
unless as a device to remove them from the scene in favour of a new-
comer. It could be said that of all the erotic works of this genre,

Susan Aked approaches most closely to being additionally a feasible sex manual of its time (spermatozoa are referred to as 'tadpoles'). An American paperback edition (Pendulum Books, 1967) very curiously repeats on its title page the error of the original in spelling the heroine's name with a *z*, though this error is nowhere else committed in either edition and is not repeated on the actual cover of the contemporary paperback.

THE SOWING OF THE SEED

It was impossible for our house to remain long plunged in the depths of desolation, when once so sweet, amiable, and lovely a girl as Lucia had come into it. Naturally of a most loving and sympathetic disposition, she had, at first, been greatly grieved at the sad loss she had herself sustained by the deaths of a loving aunt and uncle. The almost tragic nature of their deaths had also a naturally inspiring effect upon her, and she was as subdued and tearful almost as Martha and I, but in less than a day she saw that if she were to be of any use she must overcome her own feelings, so as the better to raise our spirits. At first all our conversation was of the beloved parents, now, as I fondly thought, gone to eternal bliss in Heaven. Without stating her belief on this subject, Lucia rather encouraged mine; in fact she showed the greatest tact in gently leading my thoughts from the dark grave, and the darker secrets beyond it, to this world, and its multiplicity of pleasures and delights. She insisted on our taking good long walks. The weather was open and pleasant. All nature seemed to be in accord with us—everything was well grown, but had still to reach full development. We ourselves, Lucia and I, were as it were in this condition too. It was impossible not to feel the effects of the lovely beauty of the country, of the sweet fresh air, of the song of the birds, and with exercise came back a more elastic state of health, and as my body improved in health so did my mind. Lucia in old times had sneered at beetles, and weeds, and stones, and rubbish, as she called the results of my natural history rambles, but now she appeared to take a delight in all I had to tell her about these things. I do not believe she knew a word of science, but she was so quick and intelligent, and seemed so anxious to learn, that I soon found myself growing quite excited in my eagerness to teach her, and if I referred to my dead parents it would be merely to tell Lucia what they had said about these matters, not to wail and lament as I had first done. So some three weeks passed away, and July was upon us, with hotter sun and warmer air. We used to be glad to find some glade in the woods, near a purling brook, where we could sit or lie down on the grass, and talk. One day when thus situated Lucia said:

'Susan! do you intend to live here all your life?'

'Well!' I answered, 'I suppose so. Where should I go, and why should I not stay here?'

'Oh!' she said, 'now, my dear, without meaning to be at all rude to you, I don't think I could live here much longer'.

'Oh! Lucia! You are not thinking, I hope, of going away yet! What should I do without you, my own darling cousin!' and I began to cry.

'There! There!' said she, putting her arm round my waist and kissing me. 'I would not have said that if I had had any idea it would have made you cry, darling. What I meant was, this is such a lonely spot! You never see a soul here from morning to night. I declare I have been here nearly a month, and except old Penwick, I have not seen a single gentleman inside the house. Are there no families with young men living near enough to have discovered the lovely violet called Susan Aked, who hides her beauteous charms in these secluded groves?'

She spoke half in earnest, half in jest, so I said:

'Now Lucia! Don't make fun of me. I may live in a very secluded spot, but I don't see why you should find fault with people for not taking notice of such an insignificant girl as myself'.

'But Susan! You are not insignificant. You are perfectly lovely, if you only knew it! Now, let me speak! If you saw more people you could not help noticing, if no one happened to tell you, that you are beautiful. Yes, beautiful! Your eyes are something perfect, and so is your face. You have lips which no man can resist longing to kiss! You have a lovely figure, a perfect bust, or one which will soon be perfect when your breasts have grown a little more full; as it is I can see plainly through your dress that the high, hideous, stiff stays you wear cover two most charming little globes. Ah! why don't you get others, like mine for instance, which give all necessary support without preventing the rounded globes being seen? It is really a shame to spoil a bosom like yours, and a girl ought to take care of charms which have so powerful an influence over the imagination of men'.

'Oh goodness! Lucia! How you do run on! Now do you think I care a straw what men may think of me! As for my stays, poor mamma bought them for me, and I think she was good enough judge of what I required'.

'Ah! bless you, Susan dear! Now I would not mind betting that, had poor Aunt Maria lived to see you in society, she would soon have looked to your being dressed so as to show off your lovely points to advantage'.

'But suppose I don't care for society, and never wish to go into it'.

'Oh! But Susan! You are talking of what you know nothing about. In a girl like you society means great admiration, and who is there who does not like to be admired?'

'Well! I don't care about it, for one!'

'My dear child, for you are a child and nothing else, in spite of all your science, and botany, and stuff, you have been so buried here, that unknown to yourself, you have grown up in complete ignorance that there is a world of men and women about you, and that some day, perhaps not far off now, you will have to take your place in that world. When you do, you will, I venture to prophesy, very soon find out what a charm there is in being admired. But, as I asked you before, are there no young men in these parts?'

'No! Lucia! I don't believe there are. We lived so very quietly, that I suppose if there are any such creatures, they never found us out. Our parish is quite a small one, and, as you may have seen in church, there are very few people in it, and no gentry. Papa used to be called "The Squire" '.

'And you actually contemplate without horror the idea of living here by yourself all your life?'

'Oh, no! I hope you will come sometimes and see me, Lucia. I shall ask Gladys, too. Besides, I have old Martha, and I have my birds, and beasts, and flowers in the summer; my piano and my books in the winter; and my poor people to look after. You have no idea of how very busy I am usually'.

'But Martha won't be always with you. Gladys and I, I am sure, would be glad to come and stay with you sometimes; but, Susan dearest, I know Gladys well, and she would soon mope to death here where she would see no one of the opposite sex. Besides, her tastes

are not half so countryfied as mine, and I declare to you that, much
as I love you, I do not think I could live here much longer without
being tired of myself, and even of you. Women require men just as
much as men require women. If you had some handsome agreeable
young squires down here it would be pleasant enough to spend the
days flirting in the fields and woods with them, but there is not
a soul!'

'My goodness! Lucia! How you do care about men! Now I
declare I should not mind it, if I never saw another in my life!'

'That is because you have never known a town, my dear Susan.
You have never known what it is to be wooed! You don't know the
pleasure of courtship. You don't know what it is to have man wor-
shipping the very ground you have walked on. In fact you have
never dreamt of love'.

I was silent.

'Well!' she continued, 'now have you?'

'I really do not understand a word of what you are talking about,
Lucia. To me a man is nothing, and as for love, except the love of
my parents, or of you, or of dear old Martha, I know nothing.
You mean something, I am sure, of which I have never heard. Of
course a husband loves his wife, a parent his child, but I can't see
what there is in such love to rave about as you do!'

'Have you never read any novels nor any love stories, Susan?'
she went on.

'No! My father and mother said they were foolish stuff'.

'I have heard them say so. And have you not even Sir Walter
Scott or Shakespeare in the house?'

'Shakespeare we have, I know; but it is locked up in papa's study,
in the glass bookcase. I have never read it'.

'Ah! then read "Romeo and Juliet", and you may perhaps learn
a secret or two'.

'The secret of love? But what is this curious secret, Lucia?'

'Well now, Susan? answer me! You are a girl, are you not?'

'Yes, of course I am'.

'Of course you are! But why "of course?"'

'Well, because I am, I suppose! I was born so. I don't know
any other reason'.

'Well, but there is a very good reason, if you only knew it. Why
should you be formed different from a man for instance? Can you
tell me that, sweet Susan?'

'I don't know, but what difference is there?' Lucia stared at me with very open eyes.

'Oh! come! Susan! You don't mean to pretend that you have lived so long without knowing that there are most marked differences between a man and a woman?' So saying she reached out her hand, and lightly placed it in my lap, pressing her fingers on the part between my thighs. 'Now are you not immensely different from a man *here?*'

Of course I knew I was. I knew that a man was not formed there as I was, but I tell the truth if I say I did not then know *exactly* what the formation of a man was.

'And have you never wondered why you should be formed here as you are?' keeping her hand still pressing between my thighs, whilst she gently stroked the place with her long tapered fingers.

'No, indeed I have not! But, Lucia darling, don't do that!'

'Why not? You are a girl and I am another. Surely one girl may touch another there? What harm is there in it?'

'I don't know whether there is any harm, but oh!'

'What's the matter?' said Lucia, her colour rising slightly.

'My dear girl! Oh! For goodness' sake take away your hand! You are tickling me dreadfully! Oh! Now! Don't go on, or you will make me scream!'

'Scream away, my pet!' said Lucia, laughing. 'You may spend your breath, if you like, that way, but I mean to make you spend something else before I am done!'

I did not understand her; in fact, the pleasure she gave me was so intense, and at the same time seemed to me so shameful, that between the two feelings I was nearly distracted. In vain did I try to tear myself away from her. Lucia held me tight with one arm, whilst she half lay upon me, laughing and looking into my eyes as if she expected to see something she wanted to find in them. Very soon the tickling reached such a point that I felt myself as it were jump under her hand, a thrill, a throb shot through all that region, a delicious sense of some pent up flood bursting the ever lightening bonds which had held it back, made itself distinctly felt, and so great a sensation of delightful languor took hold of me that I could not resist giving vent to a grateful, 'How nice that is!'

Lucia took her hand off, and throwing herself completely on me, she pressed me enthusiastically in her arms, kissing me with the most passionate affection.

196

'Ah!' she said, 'so my darling Susan is sensitive to pleasure! I
thought a girl made like her must be. Oh! Susan! Susan! Would
that I were a man! Would I not make you happy! And myself too!'

'Well,' said I, 'please do get off me, Lucia! I am nearly choking,
and your weight is perhaps heavier than you think. Ah! now I can
breathe!

My room was lighted by one high window, and on one side of this
window was the press in which I hung my clothes. It had a broad
door, and that door was a large mirror, fully six feet high. I was
a girl of nature. Had I ever bathed near this mirror I should have
often seen myself naked reflected in it, but as a matter of fact, it
never struck me that it was worth while to take the trouble to walk
from the corner of my room, where my bath was always placed
for me, to look at my naked charms in this glass. I used it occasionally when I dressed with extra care to go to church, or to go into
Worcester, or to Malvern, but I was not much given to admire myself in any glass.

I had no idea that I was beautiful, and I did not care for my
face. But Lucia, who was very artistic in her taste, and no mean
hand with brush and pencil, at once saw an opportunity for a
pretty picture. She drew the curtains of the window so as to form
only a broad chink, through which light enough would shine to
illumine any object near the window, but not so much as to cause
any powerful reflections from the walls, and then so placed herself
and me, side by side opposite the mirror. I was delighted. I had
never seen anything so perfectly lovely as we looked in that glass.
Two naked nymphs with the most graceful forms, glowing with
life, showing all that makes beauty most bewitching, rosy cheeks,
cherry lips, glistening eyes, necks and arms and thighs of polished
marble, breasts looking each a little askance, tipped with rosy
nipples, skins as pure as snow but lighted with the faintest rosy tints,
as of light reflected from a dying sunset sky, and forms which shone
out against the dark background, sharp, yet softly lined, and clear
as the light of day. Oh! What a mistake artists make in failing to
ornament the soft rising triangle beneath the curve of their beauties'
bellies with the dark curling hair that Nature has provided, surely
to enhance the lovely slope which leads to the entrance of the
Temple of Love. The contrast afforded by this dark, bushy, little
hill, and the surrounding white plain of the belly, or the snowiness of
the round voluptuous thighs is really exquisite. And why do painters

and sculptors neglect the soft, inturning folds, which form that deep, quiet looking line that retreats into the depths between the thighs, half-hidden by the curling locks, but plain in nature, and to deprive woman of which would take from her her very essence? They don't do it to men. I have seen statues and pictures in which all that a man has are represented with striking fidelity, if partly idealized: why then should it be indecent to picture woman's most powerful charm. It cannot surely be said that what men most prize in her is too ugly to be drawn.

Lucia was wild over her lovely picture, as she called it. She put herself and me into various attitudes and admired, as indeed did I, all that the faithful glass reflected. I could not help noticing, however, that her form showed greater maturity than mine, but she told me that there were few girls of my age who could compare with me in that quality, and that in a very short time, some few months, my shoulders and hips and limbs would be as round as hers.

'As for your bosom, Susan, I would not wish to see it one atom more developed. I should like you to keep those exquisite little bubbies just as they are. Let them grow just a trifle firmer, perhaps, but not one atom larger. See! A man's hand could hardly completely cover one. They just have sufficient prominence to fulfil the law of beauty, and they look so imploringly at one as though to say, "Please squeeze me! Please kiss me!" Your motte I should like to see just a trifle more plump, another quarter of an inch rise would do it no harm, and be more agreeable for a man to feel when he drives home the last inch, or squeezes in the last line after the short digs'.

'I am beginning to understand,' said I. 'But Lucia, now you have the opportunity. No one is near, tell me all about a man, and what it is he does to one. What are short digs?'

'I'll sleep with you tonight, my pet,' she said, kissing me. 'But I shall have so much to tell that I won't spoil the fun by beginning now. 'Now,' she added, 'come, dress and put on my stays, and I'll put on yours, and we will go and exhibit ourselves to Mrs. Warmart'.

Lucia made me put on her stays and dress, and she herself put on mine. We were much of the same height and build, only, as I have before said, she was everywhere a little fuller, more rounded, so to say, than I. Both she and I were surprised to find that her dress was not in the least too full in the bosom for me, and it was not simply the stays which made the fit apparently correct, for my own bubbies quite filled up the bags in them; in fact, had they been made for me, her stays could not have fitted better. But it was different with her when she put on mine. Her poor darling, lovely bubbies were simply squashed out flat, and yet she could hardly get my dress to fasten over her bosom.

'Oh!' she cried, 'the brutal instrument of torture! I will wear it for a few minutes just to show Martha, but no longer. After that, Susan, my dear, we will change again. I wonder how you could have endured such a strait jacket as this, or how on earth your bubbies ever came to be so sweetly round and pointed as they really are. Mine are crushed!' Then looking me over, she exclaimed at the beauty of my figure, which was now shown off, she said, to perfection, and had a chance of appearing at last as it should. We ran downstairs to Martha, who, busy at some household work, looked up and mistook me for Lucia.

Lucia was delighted.

'Ah! Susan, I told you so. Now look, Mrs. Warmart, I am not going to let Susan wear those abominable stays any longer. I know I have a good figure, yet first look at me! Did you ever see such a lout of a girl as I look! Positively you would never think I had any breast at all, and I declare I hardly thought Susan had any either. Yet see! Just feel the lovely little ducks! Firm, round, elastic: such a pair of pretty doves with little rosy bills! It is downright shameful to crush them in such a wooden box of a corset as this. I know my breast is actually hurt under it'.

'Well, you see, Miss, it was all her ma's wish. She never liked Miss Susan to look grown up and developed'.

'But why? Why on earth? Anyone could see that she must be quite ripe. Look at her hips'.

'Ah, well! She had a good reason, my dear young lady'.

'Perhaps she had, and perhaps she had as good a reason why poor Susan should be condemned to wear drawers which must be exceedingly incommodious at certain times, to say the least of it!'

'Well, yes, Miss. There was the same reason for that, too. I hardly like to say before Miss Susan, because she is innocent like. Yet she ought to know to be on her guard'.

'Well, Martha, since Susan is quite old enough to know what is what, you might tell us the grand reason'.

'Well, miss, when Master Charlie Althair lived at The Broads, people said that there were not two greater pests than him and

Jack Cocklade, who lived in Leigh. I do believe Master Charlie got credit for doing more than he did, but all the people complained that no sooner did their daughters get fledged than either he or Jack would be into them, and that ripe maidenheads could not be found, high or low! What Master Charlie did not pluck, Jack did. No one ever brought an affiliation case against Master Charlie, but Jack is known to be father of ever so many love children. Poor Miss Mary Essex was raped by one or other of 'em in her own father's field, not half a mile from home. I believe that it was Jack who did it, but there was a great noise a little time after, when she and Master Charlie were caught by Mr. Essex hard at it in one of his barns. They were caught in the very act, and it was that which caused Mrs. Althair, who had no idea until then what a lively lad he was, to go away from The Broads. I believe she had to pay up handsomely for that little spree of her son's, and being a very strict and straight lady, she could not face the people after her disgrace, as she called it. Jack, indeed, got imprisoned for his share, because Miss Mary Essex confessed he had had her before Master Charlie and against her will; but he was let off pretty easy because she had to admit that she did love being had by Master Charlie. This happened some five or six years ago, and poor Mrs. Aked got such a shock she wouldn't let Miss Susan out by herself, nor allow her to have her drawers divided at all. But poor Miss Susan complained she could not do her jobs easy when she had to unbutton her drawers behind, so she had them cut as you find them now'.

I saw that Lucia was dying with internal laughter, and I felt beetroot-red with shame. But more and more I understood what was said about Charlie Althair and Jack Cocklade, and why my drawers were made as to cover my cunnie completely when not partly loosened.

'Well, Martha,' said Lucia, 'I think Susan can defend herself in the future. So anyhow I am going to take it on myself to drive her to Worcester tomorrow to look for a decent pair of stays, and as she is so uncomfortable in her drawers, we will cut them up in front and make them as they should be'.

'I'm much afraid you can't go to Worcester tomorrow, my dear young lady, because the horse has gone to be shod, and won't be back till tomorrow afternoon. Bill coachman is going to Hereford to see his wife's mother, and said he would not be here till tomorrow evening, but the brougham will be ready for you the next day after'.

'Well, so be it. We can wait a day. Come, Susan. Now for goodness' sake, let me have my stays again!'

So off we trotted upstairs once more. I admired myself in the glass until Lucia had taken off her dress, and then, with a sigh, I yielded her own, and once more clad myself in my old habiliments.

Agreeable to her promise Lucia came to my bedroom after Martha and the servants had gone to bed. She sprang into my bed and clasped me in her arms and kissed me repeatedly, and said: 'Oh, Susan! We will have such a night of it. I'll tell you all you want to know, and I will show you more, and I will prove to you that it is downright folly to loose years of youth, which can be so well turned to profit by using the charms and senses nature has given you'.

Sadopaideia

technical outsider to our period, *Sadopaideia, Being the Experiences of Cecil Prendergast, Undergraduate of the University of Oxford, Showing how he was led through the pleasant paths of Masochism to the Supreme Joys of Sadism* c. 1907, is nevertheless so in debt to its Victorian predecessors as to admit inclusion.

There is little or nothing of originality in the story which belongs to what might be called the school of romantic flagellation rather than that of the type of writing devoted to flagellation in which acts of sex are totally submerged or non-existent and in which frantic alphabetical acrobatics are performed by the authors to produce onomatopoeic representations of screams, cries and the sound of whips ascending. The style of *Sadopaideia* is closely comparable to that of *Susan Aked* (c. 1898) and is quite possibly by the same anonymous author.

American paperback editions have appeared from Grove Press and Pendulum Books (1967).

JULIETTE'S STORY

'Well,' said Juliette, 'my father died suddenly and we found we were left awfully poor'.

'You must begin long before that,' said Muriel. 'It began with my leaving South Parade. You see, Maude never forgave me for winning Juliette from her and tried all she could to pay us out. There was no other little girl left without a senior, and no senior would share her mignon with her, as was sometimes done. She didn't tell about the games at night in the dormitory, for that would have brought down on her head the vengeance of all the seniors, for we were all tarred with the same brush, and she was an awful coward. But she hated us both, Juliette because she could never get her to make love to her gladly, and me because she saw Juliette was quite eager to do anything to or for me. So things went on for about a year, until one hot summer's day in the garden I couldn't wait till night, and Juliette and I were having quite a nice little *flirtation* on the grass, which was rather long. Maude must have spotted us and told Mrs. Walter, for we were suddenly startled in each other's arms by her voice. 'What conduct is this?' There she stood looking down on us. 'Get up at once. Juliette, do up your drawers; go and wash your hands and then come to my room'. When we got there, she stormed at us, and talked about expelling us publicly. But I wasn't afraid of that'.

'Two hundred pounds a year each,' sniggered Juliette.

'Precisely. So she jawed a lot and at last said that in consideration for our parents, and the disgrace, etc., she would let us off with a flogging, but we must never do it again, would we promise? Oh, yes, of course we would—and we never did—in the garden. She asked us if the other girls did the same sort of thing, and of course we said no, and then she asked me how I knew of such things. I said a servant at home. 'I expected as much,' she answered. Looking back now, I, of course, realize she was *one of us* herself, for she gloated over the details and her eyes glowed as she talked. Anyhow, we got our whipping—a private one, because she did not want to publish our disgrace and get the matter talked about, for fear of putting ideas into the girls' heads'.

'Was the whipping severe?'

'Pretty well. I'd had plenty in my time. She loved whipping me, she told me later, after I left the school'.

'She spanked you, didn't she?'

'Yes, she always spanked us little girls. She used to put us across her knees, turn our clothes up, let down our drawers, and use her hand or the back of a hair brush. My word, it hurt, too. I couldn't sit down for over a week with any comfort'.

'But we paid Maude out, didn't we?'

'How was that?'

'Oh, that evening, we held a court martial in the dormitory. We bribed the maid not to turn out the gas for half an hour, and we *tried* Miss Maude. Naturally all the seniors were eager to punish the sneak, and she was condemned to run the gauntlet and to be whipped by her two victims. It *was* fun. Picture this kid of twelve,' pointing to Juliette, 'laying into the fat behind of a girl of eighteen'.

'I can't hit hard enough,' she nearly sobbed in her excitement. 'I can't hurt her enough'. I think, however, she managed pretty well, for Maude wriggled as we held her down. Then I had my turn, and at last, she had to run naked three times up and down the dormitory between two lines of girls armed with canes. She was marked all over from her shoulders to her knees, both back and front, for she fell down more than once, and the blows never stopped. She didn't dare tell, however, and left at the end of the term, and so did I'.

'Before the next term began, Juliette's father died, as she told you, when I heard of it, I got my mother to have her to stay with us, and be taught by my sister's governess. When mother died, and I was married, I still kept her with me as my sweetheart and companion—my old fool of a husband suspected nothing—and here we still are'.

'And she still lets you ...'

'Whip her? Yes, habit is strong, and she never became a senior with a mignon of her own'.

'I rather like that duel idea,' I said. 'I'd like to see one'.

'I daresay you would, but there's no mignon to fight for ... unless ...' and she looked at me.

'Unless what?'

'Unless you play the part of the mignon. Yes, that would do. You be the mignon and Juliette and I will fight for you. Come on, Juliette, undress him and perch him up ... We'll put him on the piano'.

They seized hold of me laughing and I let them strip me and stood on the baby grand piano, while they quickly took off their own clothes and got a couple of towels from the bedroom. The account of their school experiences had quite excited me, and I should have made quite a good scarecrow in a Roman garden.

There was certainly no *inutile lignum* about me, what there was was *utilissimus* in the highest degree.

They pushed the furniture back so that there was a clear space. 'Ready?' said Muriel. *'En garde'*. They held the towels in their right hands, crouching slightly forward. 'No hitting above the belt,' said Juliette. Muriel answered with a flick which just missed Juliette's right thigh. Quick as lightning Juliette flicked her towel upwards and just caught the brown curls. 'Little cat, that's the worst of teaching other people tricks'. She dodged and feinted and at last seizing a favourable opportunity made her towel curl around Juliette's left cheek with a resounding smack.

'Ow,' said Juliette, and she clapped her hands to the place.

'First blood to me,' cried Muriel. Juliette said nothing, but kept a wary eye on Muriel, lightly swinging the towel to and fro. Muriel feinted here and there and at last made a vicious cut at Juliette, but missed and over-reached herself. That was what Juliette was waiting for. As Muriel stretched forward, she brought her towel twice in rapid succession straight up between her legs. Muriel sprang back out of reach and rubbed herself. Then springing forward she rained a perfect hail of bows on Juliette, caring nothing for the other's attacks. She parried with her left arm and flicked here, there and everywhere. Her quickness of wrist and eye surprised me. At last two cuts, one after the other, curled quite around between Juliette's cheeks, and as the latter retired, she followed them up with a couple of back handers, both of which reached between Juliette's legs in front.

'Enough, enough, I give in,' cried Juliette, who was quite out of breath.

'Come on, Cecil. You're mine'.

I jumped down from the piano.

'Get the cases, Juliette,' Muriel said.

'What,' I said. 'Do you think you're going to whip me?'

'Mignons are always whipped ... Do let me, just this once ... you can whip me afterwards if you like ... Besides, this is only a love whipping'.

'No,' I said. 'I tell you what. We'll have a triangular duel. I'll take the two of you on, and whoever gets the first cut home shall give his opponent five cuts. Towels or birches, you can choose your own weapons'.

'Towels for me,' said Muriel. 'They're longer'. 'Birch for me,' I said. 'Now come on'. I waited for their attack, and as I expected, I easily dodged Juliette and parried Muriel's flick with my birch and before she could recover, flicked her with the twigs between her legs. 'One, get down on the couch, Muriel'.

She obeyed. 'Not too hard, dear'. I gave her five moderate cuts and she got up.

'Round two,' I said. This time Muriel was not so eager. She kept a wary eye on my birch, so that I could not get her towel and entangle it. Juliette kept me busy flicking here and there. At last I thought I saw an opening and cut at her; I missed and quickly both towels came round me, one on each side. Muriel shouted for joy.

'Come on, Juliette, it's our turn now'. I could not in honour refuse or resist, but with as good a grace as I could, lay down on the couch and took my five strokes from each of them. Neither of them tried really to hurt me, but made the birch curl wickedly between the cheeks and thighs.

'Round three, now look out, Juliette'. She was evidently enjoying it and laughed. Cut and parry followed each other for a minute or two. I dodged this way and that and at last more by accident, I fancy, than anything else, managed to flick Juliette's thigh. It was only just a graze, but it counted. She received her five strokes and wriggled with pleasure and pain.

We were all of us out of breath with laughing and the exertion. I threw myself into the chair. Muriel collapsed on the couch beside Juliette. The latter put her arms round her and hugged her. They certainly made a lovely picture with their bodies closely entwined. I sat and watched them, but the sight of their naked bottoms proved too much for me, and when I saw Juliette's right hand steal down between Muriel's legs, I got up softly and took the webbing from the case. Muriel's eyes were shut and Juliette lay half on top of her kissing her, her fingers very busy. I reached over them and before they knew what I was doing I had slipped the webbing underneath Muriel and tied them tight together. 'You naughty children,' I said in a gruff voice. 'I'll teach you. You're not at South Parade now'. And down came the birch on Juliette's plump little cheeks. She kicked and squirmed, and turning away to avoid the blows, brought Muriel's bottom into sight as she turned with her. I was not slow to take advantage of this new field of action.

'Mind my knuckles, though,' said Juliette as one cut reached far up between Muriel's legs.

'They shouldn't be there'. Muriel was now on top, and getting most of the blows. She had also got her hands round Juliette and was busily untying the knot.

She succeeded at last, and jumping up saw the case. 'Come on, Juliette. We'll pay him out for that trick'. They had both seized birches and made for me. I had my work cut out to avoid them, and we all chased each other round the room, slashing and cutting at each other with all our might. Very few of the blows proved effective, and at last, worn out with laughing and the chase, we all fell on the couch helpless. Then a less fierce but no less tiring orgy ensued, ending as usual in the bath. This, by the by, was built on the Roman plan of white marble with steps leading down into about four feet of water. It was a hobby of Muriel's husband, and was quite big enough for three or four people at the same time. It was more like the 'plunge' at a Turkish Bath than the ordinary bath of today. The only drawback to it was that it took rather a long time to fill, and the water was never really hot. Still, as Muriel used to say, it was usually hot enough outside in her boudoir and it was good to have something to cool one.

* * * * *

'So Juliette has been with you ever since she left school,' I said to Muriel, after we had bathed and Juliette had gone to get tea.

'Yes, she came home to me, as I told you, to work with my young sister, and when I got married to Anthony, I had her with me as my companion and sweetheart, though Anthony never suspected that, and if he had, I shouldn't have cared'.

'But she's not a virgin, and she never married, did she?'

'Ah! Now, that's rather a tragedy, though it has its funny moments. Would you like to hear about it?'

'Rather!'

'Well, we have long gaps in our family. I've one brother twelve years older than myself and one sister six years younger, and that's all. George was married when I left school and Elsie was quite a child, younger than Juliette. But I had a cousin, Harry, just about Juliette's age, two years older, to be exact. He stayed with us one holiday when he was about seventeen. I was, of course, grown up and had "come out". Anthony was beginning to hang around, but he hadn't definitely proposed to me. Juliette and I were sweethearts, then as now, and though we did not share bedrooms, our rooms were next to each other, and you can imagine we spent most of the time in each other's arms. Harry evidently suspected our goings on, as you will see, and he was as hot as you make 'em himself. But he was very clever. I never had the slightest suspicion, until the discovery. We used to be quite free and easy together. I used to tease him terribly, and delighted in seeing him grow uncomfortable, and change his legs and move about on his seat. He told me afterwards that he didn't dare try any games on with me, although he wanted to badly. I was too grown up for him to tackle. But one night he saw Juliette going to my bedroom after we had all gone to bed, and he listened at the door. Our rooms were quite away from Mother's, and, as we never thought about Harry suspecting we made no attempt to moderate our voices, and our exclamations of pleasure. He stood and listened at the door and heard everything, and I can assure you there was a good deal to hear. Luckily there was no whipping that night, or the sequel might have been different, but you can imagine he heard enough to leave no doubt as to what we were doing. Anyhow, the situation was too much for him, and, as he told me, he played a lone hand by himself on the mat outside, and then, growing nervous lest he should be discovered, retreated to bed, where his sleep was not as undisturbed as it might have been.

Looking back after the denouement, I remember that he looked most intently and meaningly at us the next day, but at the time I paid no attention to it. We played our usual game of hide and seek in the twilight in the garden, with the usual kisses for forfeits when caught. He certainly kissed me with more meaning than usual, but nothing more. With Juliette, however, he was much bolder, for she told me that his hand became very venturesome and once even tried, when he caught her, to investigate her most secret charms. Of course, at that time she was wearing shut up drawers, so he couldn't get much satisfaction. She was very excited when she told me, and by no means as angry with him as I thought she ought to have been. I grew quite angry and jealous and threatened her with a whipping if she let it happen again. She promised she would not, but I determined to watch.

That night I was prevented from my usual delights with Juliette by the ordinary periodical disability we poor women are cursed with, so Juliette knew it was no good coming to me. I was so angry and jealous though, about her letting Harry take liberties with her that I couldn't sleep, and I decided that I would give Juliette a whipping—not severe—but enough to relieve my feelings and to warn her as regards the future. So I got out of bed, took a birch from my trunk where I always kept one safely locked up, and went to Juliette's room.

When I got to the door I was thunderstruck at hearing voices. 'Oh, don't, Harry. You're hurting me ... no, don't ... you can't get it in, it's too big ... use your fingers ... no ... no ... I can't bear it ... you're tearing me in two ... oh ... oh!' I burst into the room and switched on the light. What a sight met my eyes. I could see nothing of Juliette, except her legs, which were wide apart, with the knees in the air, and between them Harry's back and bare legs, with the pajamas round his ankles, moving vigorously up and down. Before he had time to stop I rushed to the end and brought the birch as heavily as I could down on the heaving buttocks. 'You cad,' I cried. 'Get off. How dare you violate that child?' He sprang off and away and I saw at a glance that I was too late. Juliette's legs and mount were all red with blood, the damage had evidently been done. But I was just in time to prevent still worse mischief, for as he stood shamefacedly before me, great jets of his manhood spurted from his arrogant weapon. This was, of course, the first time I had seen a man in this condition, and I was naturally very excited. In fact, I felt the bandage I was wearing was soaking with a different fluid from that for which I was wearing it. But I was too mad with anger and jealousy to pay much attention to that at the moment. I went to the door and shut and locked it and then turned to Harry, who was stooping to gather up his pajamas. Juliette was still lying on her back, but she had turned her head away, covering her face with her hands and sobbing.

'Now, what have you to say for yourself?' He remained mute. 'I shall tell Mother of this the first thing in the morning, but that won't do much good. Juliette's ruined, you've taken her virginity, if you haven't seriously injured her. What reparation can you make? It's absurd to talk about marriage, for you are both far too young. You beast! You cad!' I raved at him. 'How dare you corrupt an innocent girl?'

'Not so much of an innocent,' he broke in. 'I'm sorry I took her maidenhead. I never thought she would have one'.

'What do you mean?'

'Well, I listened at your door last night, and heard what was going on in there between you and Juliette, so you see it's no good coming the innocent over me. And what's more, Miss Muriel, if you tell Auntie about me, I'll split on you two'.

'I don't know what you mean,' I said, 'but anyhow, she wouldn't believe you. We should both deny it, and that wouldn't do you any good. You would be sent home, and if I know anything of Uncle Harry, you'll have the finest thrashing you've ever had in your life. Now I'll tell you what I'll do. I don't want any scandal. If you'll submit to be punished by me and promise faithfully not to do that to Juliette again—why, you might have given her a baby, if I hadn't come in—and to marry her, if she will have you later, when you are in a position to marry—well, I'll say nothing to Mother. If you refuse, I go to Mother at once'.

'You punish me? How?'

'With this, and a cane I've got. I mayn't be as strong as Uncle Harry, but I'll do my very best.

'I'm not afraid of you,' he laughed. 'You can do what you like to me, and as for Juliette, I'll promise both those things'.

'Very good,' I answered. 'Come here'.

I led him over to some hooks which were on the wall and made him catch hold of two of them. I found Juliette's stockings and tied each wrist as tightly as I could to a hook. His pajamas trousers were still round his ankles and the short jacket, strained by the position of his arms, left his bottom well exposed. 'Now,' I said, 'we'll see whether I can do any good'. And I rained a volley of blows with the birch all over both cheeks. He stood the punishment stoically, and I grew vicious. I became more deliberate, choosing my spot for the cuts carefully and at last, one or two proved efficacious, for he wriggled a bit and said, 'Here, that'll do, Muriel'.

I laughed. 'Do? I've not begun yet'. I noticed that the birch was getting worn out and looking about me saw Juliette's riding whip lying on the chest of drawers. It was a dainty little thing, quite light, but made of whalebone, bound with silk. I put down the birch and picked up the whip. The first cut right across both cheeks was evidently a surprise. He gave an involuntary cry of pain. 'Here, what's that you're using?'

He turned around to look as another cut fell just where the first had fallen. 'Here, I say, that's enough'. 'Enough? Not half. I'll teach you to rape virgins. If I can't repair the injury, I'll make you suffer, your blood shall help to wipe out Juliette's. There, there, and there. Don't you wish you had chosen Uncle Harry?' He made no attempt to conceal now his pain. 'You'll cut me to pieces, you cat. Oh, oh, oh God!' as a very vicious cut curled by chance between his plunging, kicking legs and flicked the hanging bag. His cries of pain spurred my energy. I redoubled my blows and his cries of pain and rage changed to sobs and appeals. 'Muriel, please no more. You'll cut me to bits. Let me off now. I swear I'll marry Juliette. I'll never touch her again, Muriel darling, for God's sake. Oh, my God, have pity. Mercy, mercy, mercy'.

Juliette had somewhat recovered, and was sitting up watching the scene, frightened but excited. She had never seen such a whipping before. She joined her entreaties to his. 'Oh, Muriel, don't hurt him too much. Look, his bottom's bleeding'. She came to me and tried to stop me. I cut her across the bottom. 'Don't interfere. Your turn will come next. I'll teach you to have a lover'. She ran back to the bed, and I turned again to Harry. Certainly I had been severe. I must have given him fifty cuts and his poor bottom and thighs were a mass of weals. Here and there the skin was cut and there were little trickles of blood oozing down the skin. I felt just a little frightened, so I put aside the whip and took up the birch again. It had quite a different effect to what I expected. It must have hurt, but after the first few blows, Harry's cries changed in tone. Deep 'Ah's' and 'Oh's' followed each cut, but he no longer kicked and squirmed. He moved his loins backward and forward, just as I had seen him on the bed. I was interested and looked to see what he was doing. To my surprise, his weapon was rampant again, and by his plunging he seemed to be trying to swing it up and down, his eyes were half closed. In my curiosity I reached out my left hand to touch it. I just put my hand around it. 'Oh, you darling,' he murmured and plunged vigorously. Again the thick jets of life burst from him and he collapsed against the wall, hanging by his wrists.

I was startled and now a little frightened, so I untied his wrists. He fell on me with his arms around my neck, sobbing and calling me his queen. He slid down on his knees and bending down kissed my feet, uttering at the same time words of love and homage. This attitude completely conquered my anger. I raised him up.

'That will do,' I said. 'We won't think any more about it. You can go to bed. Now, Juliette, for you'.

'You're not going to whip Juliette?'

'Certainly I am'. 'No, you mustn't. It was all my fault. If you think she deserves punishment, punish me again for her. I'll bear hers as well as my own, if I can'. He knelt down again, and flinging his arms around my legs, kissed my feet passionately.

For the first time in my life I realized the ineffable joy of the woman dominant. I delighted in the subjection of Juliette, but she was only a girl and my mignon. But here was a man, or at any rate a boy, absolutely subservient to me. I looked down on him as he grovelled before me, gloating over him, and exalting in my power. 'Very well, then, Juliette shall escape for the present. You shall bear her punishment, and her humiliation. Take those pajamas off'. He did so. 'Now kneel down before me there, and beg my pardon and ask me to whip you'. He knelt down humbly. 'Forgive me, Muriel,' he sobbed. 'Go on. Ask for your punishment ... ask for it!' 'Please whip me,' he stammered. 'Where?' I insisted. He looked up at me. 'Wherever you like'. 'Oh? Shall I flog your manhood?' (His hand instinctively clasped his sex, protecting the tender parts.) 'Oh no, not there!' 'Where, then? On your bottom?' 'Yes, on my bottom. See, there it is, ready for you'. And he bent forward, pushing his bottom out, waiting for the strokes. 'Kiss my feet then, and keep still'.

I brought the remnants of the birch straight up and down between his cheeks six times, and at each blow he clasped my legs and kissed my feet ardently. His hands clutched convulsively around my calves and when I stopped and raised him slightly, he did not let go but slid higher, pulling my night dress up, until when he stood on his feet he had pulled it right up and held my naked body close to him. Our lips met in a long and passionate kiss. He was still sobbing from the pain—inarticulate words of adoration came from him and his touch was reverent though caressing.

'Don't touch me there,' I said suddenly, as his hand fell from my waist to where the bandage was fixed between my legs.

'Why not, my queen of women? I worship every bit of you'.

'No, you mustn't. You ought not to have seen me like this'. But it was no good. I could not stop him. His eager hand dived beneath the bandage and penetrated right into my most secret parts. He had not long to wait. The excitement of flogging him and his adoration had set my whole body on fire, and within a minute I drenched him with my life and love. I leaned forward and kissed him frankly and lovingly.

'You are forgiven, Harry. Only remember your promises'. 'I will remember,' he said, as he kissed me again. He then turned to Juliette. 'Good night, Juliette darling. Forgive me for my unkindness to you, but you shall be my wife as soon as I can marry you'. They kissed lovingly and he turned to go.

'Don't forget these,' I said, pointing to his pajamas. 'If they are found here in the morning, people will ask questions'. He smiled, picked them up and put them on.

He winced a little as the flannel touched his wounded skin, smiled a little ruefully, kissed us both again and went away to bed.

'That is how Juliette lost her virginity, Cecil'. 'But what about Harry? What became of him? He has not married Juliette'. 'No, he was drowned while bathing, poor boy, about a year after. How we've missed him. He was a natural Masochist. I have never met anyone like him. My husband liked to be ruled, but that was because he was an old man and other pleasures had palled on him, but Harry loved my power over him. I hoped when I met you that you might have taken his place'. She gave a little sigh.

'But the boot is on the other leg,' I laughed. 'Yes,' she sighed. 'I never thought I could submit to the domination of any man, but you have conquered me, Cecil. I am yours utterly, my darling, my king'.

'That's as it should be'.

'I don't know. It's all right for the present, but the future—I'm not a masochist. All my nature tends the other way, and I feel I shall want someone to subdue. Of course, there's Juliette. She's mine utterly, in spite of her revenge the other day. But I want a man—a man—'

'We must see if we can't find one for you,' I laughed. 'Provided always, of course, he doesn't interfere with my prerogative and privileges'.

'I shall always be yours, darling, no matter who there is'.

The Bagnio Miscellany

THE first known edition of this compendium carried the false date of 1792—actually c. 1830. It contained as pièce de resistance *The Adventures of Miss Lais Lovecock written by herself; and what happened to her at Miss Twigg's Academy and afterwards.* This, the longest story, was followed by *Dialogues between a Jew and a Christian, a Whimsical Entertainment, Lately Performed in the Duke's Palace,* together with *The Force of Instinct: a True Story Wherein is detailed the Curious Experiment Resorted to by a Young Lady in order to make the Hair grow on the bottom of her Belly,* with other Droll Matters and Quaint Conseits (sic). The volume was rounded off with two anecdotes: *Marie Antoinette, Queen of France* and *The Widow and the Parson's Bull.*

The first edition, containing eight plates 'finely engraved by Siddons or Seddon', according to Ashbee, was published by George Cannon who took up publishing after being a lawyer's clerk and ran his business for some forty years in the West End. Two later editions were produced by Andrew White, who like others in the Victorian underground book trade, combined publishing with bookselling in Holywell Street where trading in pornographic literature was then centred. White's editions were also illustrated, albeit 'infamously', on Ashbee's description. An American paperback editions (Pendulum Books, Atlanta, 1967) omits the two anecdotes at the end.

Of the two stories from which extracts are given here, the second —based undoubtedly on the structure and idea of *The Dialogues of Luisa Sigea* by Nicholas Chorier (c. 1660)—is remarkable for the number of other erotic works mentioned—all of them genuine and leaving no room for doubt that its author was either a collector or a bookseller.

THE ADVENTURES OF
MISS LAIS LOVECOCK

In a short time Miss Twig's Academy was broken up: for Amelia Shoveitin and Spunky Tom, and Lucy and Thickprick, had so many private conversations together, that both Lucy and Amelia were seen waddling about with big bellies, produced by the generative organs of their gallants. This could not long be kept a secret, and it finally was spread among the whole of the parents, who one after another took their daughters from such a 'sink of iniquity'.

Not long after, my mother died of typhus fever which was caught by my father, who would not allow any one else to attend on her; at length he also died, leaving me alone in the world, but mistress of a comfortable, snug fortune.

As I was between nineteen and twenty, this loss was not so severe to me as it would have been had I been younger. After paying every respect to the obsequies of my parents, my grief gradually abated, from the lovely scenes and pleasant companions with which I was soon surrounded. The servants, who had grown up with my father and mother, I presently discharged, and chose in their place a dashing young footman and coachman, and three maid-servants ripe for every fun and fancy: one Betsy Suckprick, a fine maid-girl, waited on me especially, the other two were engaged as cook and housemaid. Having now made myself complete mistress, and having none to control me, everything appeared in lustre and formed to please.

At the end of the garden there was a spacious room in which

was a beautiful bath, that during the lifetime of my father and my mother had remained unused; but I had it immediately cleared out, and the room completely furnished with sofas, mirrors, and indeed everything that could contribute to the pleasure of the salacious scenes there to be enacted.

Thus far being domiciled I soon managed to recommence my acquaintance with my old school-fellows, Sophie Frigger and Lucy Rosecunt, who (as I believe I have said before) did not live far from me; but, alas, their old sparks could not join us, nor indeed could mine, for the whole trio by this time were dispersed to the four quarters of the globe: however we had each picked up one to supply their places. They told me the way they met with theirs was this.—

As they were, one sultry summer's evening, walking in a thick wood near Lucy's house, in the midst of which ran a refreshing stream completely surrounded by high and low shrubs, they suddenly came upon this secluded spot, where they met with the beauties of nature in all variety, for they presently espied two fine, robust young men bathing themselves in the transparent stream, now floating on their backs, now swimming on their bellies. Lucy, pointing, exclaimed, 'Sophy, don't you see?' and she replied 'Don't make a noise—here's a fine large tree—it will hide us nicely, and we shall be able to see all'. But after looking some time they saw the pretty fellows whispering, and they immediately swam to a part where they were hidden from our ladies' ardent gaze by thick low brushwood; and expecting they would soon re-appear, they continued behind the tree. But the sparks had seen part of their dresses and imagined they were watching, so resolved to find out whether it was so or not, left the water and came cautiously behind our two pretty dears, who were so occupied in straining their eyes to find out where they had gone that they heard not their footsteps on the green sward till each was clasped round the waist and carried almost lifeless to a lovely secluded spot on the bank of the stream. Here the heroes disdained taking advantage of their present helpless condition, but began rallying them on their curiosity. One said, 'Well, my dears, which do you admire most—floating on the back and showing our front beauties, or swimming and showing the back settlements?' The other laughing said, 'I dare say the ladies have no particular objection to either only let it be in turn'. 'Oh, we have not seen anything to admire,' answered the girls giggling. 'I am sorry for it,' replied one of the young men, 'but now you may, my dear'. And the other spark said, 'If you saw nothing let me introduce something for you to feel and admire,' at the same time taking her hand to caress his noble machine. Things could not continue long thus, and in a few minutes they were extended on the grass, enjoying in rural manner the pinnacle of earthly bliss. As they were returning home, the young sparks disclosed their names and habitations, and discovered those of our little misses, appointing to meet them on a future evening in the same delightful spot.

I met with my new spark in a different way. There was a house directly opposite to mine in which lived my former fuckster. One summer's evening I determined to wash myself from head to foot, and being very warm I enjoyed it exceedingly, but did not apprehend that I was overlooked; for taking the precaution to see there were no lights in the house opposite, I concluded there was no one to see me, so (it being very sultry) threw up the window and began to prepare myself for my ablution, and in a few minutes stood in nature's own sweet dress. He had taken the precaution to hide his light, whereby he could the more distinctly observe my different motions. He saw me curling with my fingers the jet-black hair of my morsel. However he was not contented with seeing only, for he re-dressed himself, and getting a high ladder, placed it under my window, so that he could just reach to get in; and as it was in the country, nobody passed to see it. He jumped in, and so astonished me that I cried out 'rape! murder! robbers'. But nobody came to my assistance, of which I was afterwards glad, for I presently recognized him as my opposite neighbour, whom I had often met when walking out. 'My dear, don't be frightened,' he said; 'I won't rob you of anything; I've only come to beg'. 'What do you want,' I replied, 'at this unseasonable hour?' 'Cannot you guess?—and yet you have it in your hand—I hope to present to me;' for I was then hiding my mossy chink with my hand. 'For shame; Mr. Longstaff,' I peevishly replied, and what would you do with it?' 'Do with it?' he answered, and clasping me round the waist, he bore me to the bed, and there laid me and extended my thighs with rapture. And now I tell you, kind reader, that we did not part till morning dawned. No rosy-faced Phoebus was witness to parts of our Elysian games. He pleaded hard with me for a future treat, and I as readily granted it.

Soon after my bath was completely finished and furnished, I met

with my lovely friends, Lucy and Sophy, and appointed them to
bring their sparks with them on a certain afternoon to consecrate
the Sweet Retreat, and in the meantime apprised my hero of our
intention, that he might meet them.

The afternoon arrived. I ordered Betsy into my toilette full three
hours before the time of meeting, that she might arrange my hair
and set off my charms in their most bewitching form. Many were the
gowns, shifts and petticoats brought forward and rejected; but I
at last pitched on a very low sky-blue frock as my favourite of to-day.
I was ready for my visitors about a quarter of an hour before they
arrived, and on their arrival, as it could not be long after their hour
of dining. I invited them to take a glass of champagne. Three of these
glasses of this delectable liquor soon made us quite merry, and we
all seemed ready for anything that might heighten the pleasures of
the coming evening. Matters being in this state, I proposed a walk
in the garden, and somehow or other we in time found ourselves in
the cooling precincts of the Bath, and at length entered within its
enchanting walls. Mr. Strokar, Lucy's chevalier, thought that the
ladies would find it very refreshing to take a bath this afternoon;
and so thought the ladies but they could not think of it unless the
gentlemen would promise not to look. The gentlemen promised,
and, as might be expected, broke their promise. In a few minutes
we were promiscuously in the bath enjoying its cooling sweetness,
ourselves in Love's own sweet fever, Strokar was pointing to Lucy
an opposite mirror, where might be seen in full display her naked
beauties, while she (attempting to blush) leered upon his manly
form and members thereunto appertaining; while Sophy and her
spark, Mr. Bullstones, twining in amorous folds, were reflected on the
radiant surface of the flood in which they gambolled; and I and my
gentleman amused ourselves in every variety of salacious posture
that lust could devize, till (tired of this passive pastime) we rose,
being wiped dry by our attentive gentlemen, from the bath like
dripping Naiads; and after we repaid them for their trouble by leading them to their bashful gaze and titillating touch, till each flaming
sword was sheathed in its lovely scabbard. Oh, the amorous sighs,
the convulsive exclamations, and the bawdy dialogues that might be
heard! and the luscious charms, the wanton wriggle, and the die-
away grasp that might be seen in every part, I shall never forget!
and the latter all reflected by the surrounding mirrors. It was indeed a luxurious scene! ... After the first encounter, Lucy pulled

from off the shelf one of the birches, neatly tied with a light blue ribbon, saying, 'Why, my dear Lais, what is this here for?'

'Oh,' she replied, 'I shall presently show you. I and Longstaff mean to whip yours and Sophy's little bottom till we take all the wriggle out of them, and I think the sooner we begin the better, so Mr. Rogerwell, you just fix her on your tenpenny; and you, Mr. Bullstones, pin Sophy in the same way'.

They followed my directions, and I and Longstaff each took a rod in hand, ready to operate on their polished arses. At each renewed twitch of the birch they renewed their wanton struggles, both embraced by the arms and fixed on the pricks of their heroes, they could not release themselves, but each effort fixed them more firmly on their neddies, till by the exertion the luxurious moment came. Longstaff then threw down the birch and attacked me in the same way (standing), at each thrust smacking (as he termed it), the soft cheeks of my round little bum.

On recovering from our ecstatic trance, we determined to see what spirit we might extract from a bottle or two of champagne, and to increase our hilarity, while each damsel sat on her gentleman's knee, I ordered Betsy to strip naked and give us a *pas seul*, which she did without hesitation, and I can assure you her well-made limbs turning each lustful attitude of the dance, with her coal black crow's-nest peeping out as she turned nimble on her toe, was no mean sight, in fact, the gentlemen were well pleased with her that they thought she might further add to their lustful emotion. Each libidinous fancy was complied with, and each wanton posture tried, till we were so completely exhausted that we found it impossible to continue any longer our amorous sports, and therefore dispersed.

But poor Betsy, who had comparatively only been passive in the business, found herself so worked up that I suspect she had applied to the footman to do a little job for her, for when they had gone I directly retired to bed to recruit myself, and on passing a large store closet, where I kept my fruit, I heard a low kind of murmur, when looking through a small window in the door, found her lying her length on my store of golden pippins, with her petticoats up, inviting her gentleman by the exposure of her hidden charms, and he preparing for action.

With difficulty he brought out an immense machine, so large that he could hardly guide it to its nest—Hercules, I think, could hardly show a better. It revived the lustful fire within, and I envied Betsy her treat or teat, whichever you like, kind reader, and I hoped at some future time to take in draughts of delight from the same copious fountain.

THE FORCE OF INSTINCT

Clara.—Do men always broach us in one particular manner?

Betty.—Yes, but there are many postures. The most common one is when the lovers lie belly to belly, as we have done tonight; and it is decidedly the best posture for a young man to show his vigour.

Clara.—What other postures are there, Betty?

Betty.—'Saint George' is a favourite posture, in which the man lies flat on his back, and the girl straddles across. He then heaves and she rises up and down until she pumps up his balmy treasures. Sometimes she sits with her bottom towards his face, but more generally with her face towards his, at times leaning down and kissing him, then upright, whilst pego is battering her and producing a most powerful sensation. This sport is often repeated whilst a man sits on a chair, but it is by no means so pleasant as on a bed.

Clara.—This posture must be transporting; I should like to ride St. George very much upon a nice young man. But tell me, Betty, some more particulars.

Betty.—To enjoy a woman backwards is with some a favourite pastime; it is thus performed: The girl stoops over a bed or table, and when she is on her belly her lover turns her petticoats and shift over her back, exposing her bare buttocks to his gaze; then telling her to stand, her legs apart, he places himself between them and works away at his pleasure, sometimes standing erect and patting and shaking her buttocks, at others lying down upon her back, his hands under her to handle her bubbies. It is a method particularly adapted for the daytime, should a lady long for a stroke when she is full dressed, as it will not tumble her clothes.

Clara.—Doubtless it must be charming, but I would rather see my lover's face. What is the next posture?

Betty.—Oh, my dear, there would be no end to describing the various whims and caprices of the male sex on the occasions. They have a spoon-fashion, wheel-barrow fashion, nurse-maid fashion; but after all I consider the old-fashioned bread-and-butter fashion to be the best, because when a man is upon a woman he may turn and twist her in such a variety of ways to humour the titillation that all the postures in Aretin cannot beat it.

Clara.—What do you mean by the postures in Aretin?

Betty.—It is a book the Cambridge scholars used to shew me, containing pictures of all the changes the sexes may ring whilst in the act of copulation. But in my opinion these variations of position are only resorted to by debauchees and voluptuarians when satiated with straightforward stroking, and, as the author of 'The Battle of Venus' justly observes, they all return to the original and what appears to be the most natural mode of enjoyment again, as producing the greatest degree of pleasure.

Clara.—And what sort of a book is the 'Battle of Venus'.

Betty.—A very pretty little treatise on the various modes of enjoyment, with interesting disquisitions on the best method of exciting and gratification. I have it now at the bottom of my box, bound up with the 'Mysteries of Venus', or a description of what generally passes on a wedding night. They were given me by a sizar of Trinity College; but as I know the practical part so well, these theoretical works are no longer of use to me, and are perfectly at your service if you will accept them.

Clara.—Oh, my dear Betty, I shall be greatly obliged to you; I am sure I shall be highly delighted with them.

Betty.—But you must be very careful never to let your father or mother see them. I have several more at my aunt's, carefully locked up, they were given to me by a young gownsman, who was about to enter holy orders and get married. He was afraid to keep them by him any longer. Whilst in service at Cambridge, I used frequently to leave to go to Chesterton church on a Sunday afternoon; but instead of going there I used to meet this young gentleman at the lodging of Maria Farnham, in Wellington Row, Barnwell, where he used to stroke me, and make me read these books, and look at their pictures, in order to make me more lewd. He was a very nice young gentleman, and always paid me well. I only disliked one thing in him, which was that he always put a thin skin he called a condom over his pego before he stroked me, in order that he should not get me with child. He said as he was intended for the church, it made him more cautious; and the skin was so thin it did not at all diminish his pleasure. But as to myself, I had no fear of being with child, because I was stroked so often, and by a such a variety, and then I was mortified at being deprived of the exhilarating effect which the injection would have produced had it come into me, instead of being confined with the 'safeguard'. I used to tell him that I ought to reap the benefit of it: but all my pleas and arguments were useless; he was too timid, and would not stroke without a 'protection'.

Clara.—Then you had rare fun while you lived at Cambridge?

Betty.—Oh, yes; the majority of the people are supported by lodging such students as cannot be accommodated within the walls of the different colleges, and of course all the servant girls are seduced by these ravenous wolves. Some houses are built large and commodious on purpose to entertain more lodgers. I lived in one where no less than twenty gownsmen kept, as the local phrase is, for they do not say, I lodge or I live at Mrs. Badsock's, or Mrs. Allcock's, but they say I keep at Mrs. Slowcock's or Mrs. Grosstranger, and it was not a little droll that there should be about a dozen respectable widows who kept boarding-houses of this description whose names unfortunately terminated in the word cock—a circumstance, you may be sure, which made some fun among the students, who often amused themselves in classifying these curious appellations and deducing their derivations. There was Mrs. Hitchcock, Mrs. Whitecock, and Mrs. Flatcock, all lived in Christ Lane, Mrs. Longcock, Mrs. Pocock, and Mrs. Wilcock, in St Mary Street, Mrs. Littlecock, Mrs. Schuttlecock, and Mrs. Smallcock, in the road which leads to Trampington Causeway. But to return to the house I lived in, where I said were entertained twenty students, who all stroked me when opportunity offered. I had all times and seasons, and in all parts of the house. Sometimes when three have been breakfasting together, they have all stroked me one after another, only making me go down for something between each bout to prevent suspicion. I have had four or five slip into my bedroom and on one occasion I took a bit of chalk and made a mark behind the kitchen door to see how many times I had it into me in the course of twenty-four hours, when it amounted to thirty, but that day my mistress was out, which gave more opportunity.

Clara.—You certainly were a happy girl. I wonder you ever left so delightful a place.

Betty.—Why, my dear, I ultimately turned out on the town, and was put into the Spinning house so often by the Proctors that I got tired of it; therefore I came over to my aunt in this part of the world, where I was not known, and got into service again.

Clara.—Why, Betty, I could not have thought you had seen so much on the world. You said just now you had some more books. Can you recollect the names of any of them?

Betty.—Oh, yes, I can recollect the names of most of them, for I have read them so often I almost know their contents by heart. There was 'Fanny Hill, or the Life of a Woman of Pleasure,' 'The Power of Mesmerism,' 'Nunnery Tales,' 'How to Raise Love,' 'The Curtain Drawn Up, or the Education of Laura' (translated from the French), 'The Adventures of Sir Henry Loveall, in England, Ireland, Scotland, and Wales,' 'Manon La Foutetteuse, or the Quintessence of Birch Discipline,' 'The Spirit of Flagellation or the Memoirs of Mrs. Hinton, a School-mistress—the Exhibition of Female Flagellation,' 'The Romance of Chastisement; or revelations of the School and Bed Room,' 'The Youthful Adventurer, depicting the career of a young man among the fair sex,' 'Domestic scenes or Every one to his Taste,' 'The Romance of Lust; or, Early Experiences,' 'The Boudoir; a Magazine of Erotic Tales, and Facetie,' 'Gamiani, or two nights of Excess, by A. de M,' 'The Memoirs of a French Lady of Pleasure,' 'The story of a Dildoe, a charming and seductive tale,' 'Tit-Bits, served up, seasoned and prepared for amatory Feasts,' 'Injured Innocence, or the Rape of Sarah Woodcock, by Lord Baltimore— being the Secret History of that renowned seducer and violator, founded on facts,' 'The Philosophical Theresa, founded on the Seduction of a Young Lady by a Jesuit and the Memoirs of a Courtezan who had an imperforable Membrane, which prevented the most powerful men from broaching her,—detailing the number of times her Maidenhead was sold by the old Bawd she lived with, and describing the numerous Whims, Catrices, Letches, and Prac- tices, of the various Cullies who frequented her'. These my dear, as far as I can recollect, are the principal, with the exception of 'The Ladies Academy, or the Dialogues of Meursius,' which book appears to me to have been either the father or mother of all the rest. However, as I have taken such a fancy to you, I shall most likely give them all to you when I get married.

Clara.—Well, Betty, all I can say is this; that if you do give them to me, I will make you a present of a wedding dress in return for them. Have they got any cuts?

Betty.—Oh yes, a great many; some of them large and most

beautifully coloured. It will make your mouth water and your cunt swell to see them. There is Sir Henry deflowering Nancy Screwell, and again with Fanny in the garret, which exhibits his manly staff driving into her fringed gap in fine style; at the same time you have a most noble view of her plump, round buttocks. The riding St. George, too, which we talk about, is admirably delineated in the sofa scene, where Louise has mounted Sir Henry. The whipping scene with Misses Griffiths, Jenkins, and the widow Trevallion,—also that with Miss Athel and pupils,—are particularly luscious. The same work also abounds in rural scenes, such as Flora Campbella stroked against a bending tree, Miss Graham against a style, and Mrs. Douglas on the grass.

In the manner these luxurious girls passed many a night, until Betty, being got with child by her sweetheart, lost her place, and was obliged to marry. According to promise, she gave Miss Wharton all her books, and received in return a good rigging out, not forgetting a wedding smock, open before. It may be easily imagined that the lascivious Clara was highly delighted at the possession of such a library, and that she seldom went to bed without the voluptuarian cabinet under her pillow. There was also in the collection some French books, beautifully illustrated, which Betty had not mentioned—such as 'Anti Justine with 38 Engravings,' 'Caroline St. Hilaire' with 4 Engravings, 'Eleonore ou l'Heureuse Personne' with 6 engravings, 'Portier des Chartreux' with 27 engravings, 'Tableau des Moeurs' with 12 engravings, 'Roman de mon Alcove' with 62 engravings.